DEALER

DEALER

PORTRAIT
OF A
COCAINE
MERCHANT

by
**RICHARD
WOODLEY**

**HOLT,
RINEHART
AND WINSTON**

NEW YORK
CHICAGO
SAN FRANCISCO

PREFACE

First I must state a bias: I believe that illegal drugs should be legalized for adults, and controlled—either in the manner of alcohol, or by doctor's prescription as are the amphetamines, barbiturates, and the rest of the "medicines," or by any other method which is reasonable and appropriate. I do not wish here to argue the intricacies of these controls, precisely what they might be for which drug, how they might be designed and brought about; the aim should be simply to allow adults to ingest what they will so long as they don't hurt anybody else. We do this for alcohol—there are laws against drunk driving and so on. It should not be beyond our imagination to do the same for the other substances, and some of the illegal ones are probably less harmful in all ways than some of the legal ones.

The point is that the excesses of violence, criminality, and profit described in the following pages derive not from the drugs themselves, but from the legal prohibition of their use; it is the crime, much more than the drugs, which is damaging our society.

I am not proselytizing for drug use, nor do I condone the violence and criminality. I am only suggesting a pruning of hypocrisy so that our perception of reality in the matter may ripen. It was, in fact, a variation on this theme that first got me involved in this book.

I met Jimmy while I was on an assignment from a magazine to write an article on the economic recession as it affected New York City during 1970. The story was to be essentially an anecdotal look at the tremblings of middle-class Manhattan. But I quickly became jaded from talking to people for whom the recession was a kind of game of temporary suffering—proud agonies of searching for the cheaper cuts of meat at the A&P. And so I drifted into Harlem, where, of course, the recession was no game, but actually threatened survival for many black people who had acquiesced to pleas that they work "within the system." A friend there happened to mention to me that even the drug market was tight. At my request, and at no small risk to himself, he introduced me to his friend Jimmy, the Dealer.

After the introduction, Jimmy and I were left alone, in a sudden electric confrontation between two awesomely disparate worlds. We were seated at opposite sides of a table in the manner of a proper interview. I held on my lap the same yellow pad upon which I had been recording other notes about the recession. But neither of us was prepared to meander conversationally about in the thicket of amenities through which one usually stalks a subject. Everything in the subsequent many months proceeded from the first question I ever put to Jimmy: "Are you a drug dealer?"

It was an unusually harsh opener, but that was, of course, why he was there, and there wasn't really anything else to talk about. An hour later he returned to his world and I to mine, but I couldn't retreat fully to the recession story that the magazine wanted. So somebody else did that, and in time I got back to Jimmy and proposed that I write about him and his business. All logic and reason told him to say no, but that would have been to turn down a challenge. So Jimmy said, over a period of time, yes.

A journalist lives a strange life after all, for his life is so much the lives of others; during much of his research he is *in* the life of a movie star, a senator, an athlete, a hustler. The old rule is that one maintains a detachment, a distance, an *objectivity* while probing his subject. I believe that the most significant, albeit the most difficult, stories are those in which the author risks some personal involvement without relaxing his integrity or abandoning his responsibility to report the essence, the truth. The difficulty is that some of the truth can better be glimpsed from a distance, some from very close in.

This nettlesome balance is involved in nearly all stories. But in telling the story of someone currently involved in high-gauge criminal activity, one commits oneself to an even more troublesome bond of trust. For example, in this case the agreement was that I would do everything within my power to protect the identities of those people involved while at the same time presenting as much accurate detail as possible. Security was the only criterion. In return, I would be permitted access to Jimmy's world.

I suppose it was a rather naïve bargain on both sides. As time went on, Jimmy found that he was revealing more than he had expected to; my part became increasingly difficult because the more I knew, the more terribly difficult decisions I was finally going to have to make. I found it impossible to resist some personal involvement. I was, at times, either to be in or to be out. I chose to be in and breathe heavily.

While certain details, and certainly the people, have been disguised to some degree, I have made no attempt to hide my own participation in events. In the quest for accuracy and understanding—truth, no less—my participation was crucial. Not then to write of it would have been to persist in the same hypocrisies that are already stamped too heavily on our concerns about drugs.

Sadly enough, I cannot here thank by name those people in Jimmy's world who helped me, treated me as a friend, coached and consoled me, and—what frightened me most —trusted me. They have my deep gratitude nonetheless.

But I can at least now begin to return to my family the devotion which they have unquestioningly given me throughout the time of writing this book: to my wife Kamma, my son Jesper, and my daughter Charlotta. They withstood my moods and inattentions, and suffered my fears. And they shared those secrets which this type of story generates—a mighty burden for anyone, an especially heavy load for children of ten and seven who were required not only to still their natural curiosity but also to maintain an unnatural silence to their friends and teachers about the details of my work.

If there is to be a dedication, then, let it be to the hope that the day will come soon when all of us will be free to discuss openly all things that people do and want to do, and why. It is time, one might say, to rap straight.

R.W.

Mount Kisco, N.Y.
April 1971

DEALER

1

I shall call him Jimmy. He is thirty, and at 5′ 10″ and 190, is built like a pro football cornerback, which is what he had hoped to be. He has a trim mustache and an Afro. When he moves his head, or an arm, or a hand, it is as if his whole body adjusts slightly, ready to move in any direction, at any speed, at whatever force required; physically he is very together.

He reached under his soft brown sweater-shirt which was worn outside his slim brown custom-made trousers, and from a specially designed pocket he pulled out a small .25-caliber Browning automatic. He snapped out the magazine to expose a full clip of bullets, then snapped it back in and laid the automatic on the table between us. From another hidden pocket he produced a gold cigarette case and flipped it open. There were a row of pills and capsules, four joints of marijuana, and a dollar bill rolled in the shape of a joint. He took out the dollar bill and opened it carefully with just thumbs and forefingers, his powerful hands moving as precisely as a surgeon's. In the crease of the bill lay a narrow mound of bright white powdered cocaine, about a table-spoonful, he said, worth $150. Then he reached inside his shirt neck and pulled up a gold chain on which dangled a tiny gold spoon with diamonds in the handle. He leaned forward to reach the coke with the spoon, scooped some powder, put the spoon to his nose, and sniffed sharply, instantly emptying the spoon. He snorted two spoonfuls in each nostril—a two-and-two. Then he looked up, sprung his eyes wide open, and smiled slowly in satisfaction.

"That," he said, his words crisp and clear, "is top-shelf coke, superfly. That is why people come to me. They get *the* best. They get it when they want it. And they come back."

He picked up the automatic, extended his arm, and wheeled slowly around to face the window. He sighted along his arm and down the barrel and out the window at Lenox Avenue. Then he brought the gun back down and tucked it into his trousers so that just the tip of the butt showed, until he smoothed his shirt over that. "But they pay. Cause I come back too."

It was a serious bit of theater, an introduction to Jimmy's "flash"—what others might call style—which is crucial on the street where he earns his livelihood. It is a closely studied art, a technique of survival. Flash is in the clothes, the cars, the eyes, the walk, the talk.

"You got to have the flash," Jimmy said. "I guess it's like acting. But cats recognize the flash on the street. They get to know you by the flash. They suspect you're somebody. Like, a lot of cats on the street sort of know who I am. They know but they don't know. They know a little. 'Who's that?' a dude will say. 'That's Jimmy,' the cats will tell him. 'Oh yeah?' the dude will say."

Jimmy is a full-time hustler, whose specialty is cocaine, which he deals on a scale that may bring him $5,000 in a good week. He has a partner named Slick, whose specialty is heroin. He has a strongarm named B.J., whose specialty is karate and who collects on difficult accounts.

Hustling, dealing in illegal goods and services, is a high-risk business for high stakes, where the fast money is in Harlem. There are hundreds of hustles and thousands of

2

hustlers. Any late afternoon, along Lenox Avenue, or Seventh, or Eighth, in that area of Harlem extending north from Central Park and concentrating on the corners near 125th Street, Cadillacs begin to assemble. Custom Eldorados worth perhaps $15,000 on the straight market but often nearer $5,000 here, double-park outside the bars and restaurants. There are Eldorados with special sunroofs, all-white tires, rear windows cut in the shape of flames, interior lights of blue and red and yellow that flash on and off like Christmas trees. The flashiest of these autos often belong to the pimps. But others, two-tones with all the electronic extras such as stereo tape decks, TVs, telephones, belong to hustlers too. Jimmy has one, so does Slick. As the Eldorado is the hustler's gilded coach, so are the men and boys who wipe them off at a curbside for five dollars his footmen. Most of the cars were bought hot; so were the diamonds and gold, the furs on the women, the suits, the guns. The drivers, dressed in custom-made wear that clings and shimmers with color, and broad-brimmed hats worn at rakish angles, or applejacks—dusters—tilted forward over their foreheads covering Afros or slick hairdos, extend hands bedecked with rings and hold doorside conversations. Or they become part of the fluid movement of people in and out of the action bars, where contacts are made, deals consummated, debtors sought. The flow at first appears casual and random. But there is a cool intensity in the stares, and there are subtle and quiet eddies around certain people, by the telephone, in corners. Big-time athletes and small-time pimps, hustlers, whores, undercover cops, businessmen, and junkies share the bars, but not everybody talks to everybody. Hustlers have a hierarchy. And a stranger freezes the action like a piece of dry ice.

At one bar where Jimmy is known, where four people were shot to death in front of the pretty young barmaid over a period of a few weeks ("It's not like the Playboy

3

Club, where all the horny bastards are always trying to pinch ass," a client said. "Everybody up here is getting laid, so nobody bothers the barmaid."), a man passes slowly behind the people seated at the bar, deftly nudging each and flashing in his palm small golden boxes. "Some nice perfume for the old lady?" he says softly. The perfume may be scented water, but the fried chicken in aluminum foil, quietly hawked later, is real. Both are figuratively hot in any case, the latter literally as well, and tasty.

Outside, police cars are always in view, slowly cruising up and down the avenues. But the two cops within lounge back in their seats and ignore the Cadillacs. Foot patrolmen may stop occasionally and exchange a few words with the attendants, or even suggest that an Eldorado be moved so that somebody else's car which is blocked can get out.

Jimmy pulled aside the curtains and pointed down toward Lenox Avenue, to the heart of the hustler's Harlem. "Look out there," he said in a voice made nasal—as if he suffered a chronic cold—by the daily intake of cocaine which hammers at the mucous membranes so that they sometimes bleed. "Look at those nigger Cadillacs, all those fuckin pimps. Look at those cops. Look at those pimps and hustlers and cops. This city is the fastest city in the world, right? The fastest and the toughest. And they got the best PO-lice force, the best equipped PO-lice, in the world, right? So here I am." He swung his shoulders and snapped his fingers. "The way I look at it, I must be one of the fastest hustlers in the world, right? I gotta figure I'm one of the fastest, cause here I am." He let the curtains fall back and turned to face me, raising his eyebrows. "Right?"

Then he turned back to the window and watched a police cruiser slowly pass his Eldorado, the two patrolmen, hats off, leaning back in their seats, glancing at the car and driving on. Jimmy turned his head slowly from side to side. "Although, things are getting so tough out there . . ."

4

He took out his wallet and came over to me. "I want to show you something," he said, holding it out between us as he counted bills. There was $1,200 in hundreds and $300 in fifties. He counted it again and smiled.

"This is for the takeoff cop," he said. "You got to have something on you, cause that's the only chance you got. But if they want you, they get you. Sometimes they take your stuff and your money, and then they take you too. If they really want you, they bring their own stuff and put it on you." He touched the butt of his pistol, which was tucked in his pocket. "I ain't gonna shoot no cops unless I have to. The gun is not for the cops. The gun is for the takeoff man in the street. Like you got a lot of cats out there who got nothin to lose. Those are the cats that you have to worry about. And they don't just stop you on the street anymore and take the G or two G's you got in your pocket. They take your address book and go to your apartment and your friends' apartments and clean you all out. And then maybe they hurt you anyway."

He arched his eyebrows and spoke softly, with the hint of a smile. "That's why you got to be fast."

Late one afternoon the telephone rang. "You know who this is? I can't talk problems, not over the ding-a-ling. I'll meet you at four-fifteen at the corner of Riverside Drive and 145th Street. I know your car. See you there."

I parked in a no-parking zone where 145th Street ends in a T with Riverside Drive, and waited ten, fifteen minutes. An Eldorado parked half a block away on 145th Street, and I saw him get out and amble toward the corner, looking casually around but never at my car. He was wearing slim light-brown pants, with a woven leather belt, a green knit shirt, a green applejack cap, and leather sneakers—his "work clothes." He crossed the street, rapped on the roof of my car, and got in.

"Hey, what's happenin?" he said.

5

"It's been a long time, difficult to find you," I said.

"Mmm," he said, looking straight ahead. "Yeah, well, there's been a little fuckin up in my life. Things have been very tight, v-e-r-y tight." We sat for a few seconds in silence. Then he opened the door. "Let's take a walk," he said. "You can leave your car here. Nobody will bother it."

We meandered a few yards among the park benches over to a stone wall where we hopped up and sat, our backs to the sun and the Hudson River, facing the traffic and apartment buildings along the Drive. For some minutes we just sat in the sun and dangled our feet and looked around at the elderly people scattered here and there on the benches.

"All right," he said at last, without looking at me, "what you want to talk about?"

"About everything that's going on," I said.

He continued looking straight ahead, or to his left away from me. "Yeah, well, I been goin through so many changes, man. Sorry I couldn't get back to you, but there has been some fuckin around, and I've been very uptight for a couple of days. There are so many motherfuckers. The shit has been comin down, things get tight, I get uptight. This dude was busted, right? Dude works for one of my lieutenants. He was busted and nobody gets him out the joint right away. Like bail was about five hundred dollars, but my lieutenant couldn't find him right away because he didn't know the dude's real name. So finally he gets out the joint and he starts jivin, like, you know, he's going to blow the whistle or whatever and bring the whole thing down. So at that point I had to get involved and lay some hard stuff on everybody concerned. Like nobody wants to get shot up by me, right? They all had to understand that. See, the cat doesn't understand why he doesn't get out, and . . ."

"Couldn't you just tell him you couldn't find him, just like you're telling me?"

"Hey, listen. The dude's in jail and you can tell him a

thing, like you can tell him you couldn't find him—shit, you could tell him your mother died. In this business, nobody believes nothin. The cat is sittin in jail and he wants out. That's all he understands. But then he's just got to understand that he can't mess with you anyway, no matter what he believes. But, you know, there's always something fuckin you around, so many motherfuckers slowin up business, causin waste. It all draws heat that I don't need."

He crossed his feet, straightened out his arms, and put his strong broad hands on his knees, and leaned back, eyes closed, smiling a little, like relaxing in the sun. "My partner and B.J. are keeping an eye on things, you dig?"

"Pardon?"

"Everything's cool. They're just keeping an eye on things."

I let my eyes dart around without moving my head. Jimmy stuck his left hand into his pants pocket, and slowly pulled it partway out, exposing in his cupped palm two bundles of tiny rectangular glassine bags, each bundle held together by rubber bands. "That's what it's all about," he said, keeping an eye on the strollers and not looking at his hand. "Here in this city this is worth about, oh . . ." He figured to himself. "About fifteen hundred dollars. In Connecticut or Philly or Washington it's worth maybe seven thousand. But the trick is to find reliable people. There's so many motherfuckers. Like there were some cats in Connecticut, you know. But a cat gets the product and splits. That's just straight loss, man. Now I think it's straightened out."

A yellow Eldorado pulled slowly to the curb directly in front of us and stopped. Jimmy nodded at it barely perceptibly. "Let's take a ride."

"This is my partner, Slick," Jimmy said, nodding at the lean, angular driver, who turned, nodded politely, smiled, and said, "How ya doin?"

7

"And this is B.J.," Jimmy said, turning around in the front seat and hooking a thumb toward the silent, powerfully built man seated beside me in back. B.J. glanced at Jimmy, then turned away to look out his window. He held a paperback book in his lap.

"Tell them what you're doin," Jimmy said to me. "Just go ahead. Start at the beginning. Everything's cool."

I described my intentions and the necessary two-way trust involved. Slick nodded and said, "Mm-hm, uh-huh, yeah." Occasionally, when we stopped, he turned around. He was wearing a white applejack cap, had a bony face. B.J. said nothing, just thumbed through his paperback.

"So what you think, Slick?" Jimmy said.

"Well, uh, mmm, yeah. Well, your life does get interesting from time to time. But it's sensitive, man, very sensitive."

"No shit," Jimmy said.

Slick gave a quick wave of his right hand without looking at Jimmy. "But then," he said, "shit, you're already doin it, man, so I might as well say fuck it, go ahead."

"B.J.?" Jimmy said, turning around.

B.J. shrugged. B.J., Jimmy's collector, is about 6′ 2″, maybe 210, with short hair and a stone face. His arms and chest have undulant muscle persuasively suggested under his knit shirt. He doesn't carry a gun, but owns a black belt in karate. He didn't say anything.

At a corner we stopped, and a black man in a shiny black jumpsuit sashayed over to the car and leaned in the window. "Hey, Jim, what's happenin?"

"Hey, man."

"Jim you fucker I'm gonna shoot you," the man said, smiling.

"Fuck you gonna shoot me. What for?"

"Man, you shorted me on that brick."

"I didn't short you shit."

The man straightened up, scratched his head, looked

around, then put his arms on top of the car and poked his head back in. "Well listen now. A kilo's almost two pounds, right?"

"A kilo's more than two pounds."

"Well shit then. I'm about three ounces under."

"Then you better tell some of your dudes to stop smoking up your weed."

They both laughed and the man clapped his hands once, danced back from the car, then leaned in again. He and Jimmy mumbled about how things were going, about clothes, broads, business. Meanwhile Slick and B.J. were casing the street. On an opposite corner stood two policemen, looking around. Slick leaned over and touched Jimmy's arm. "Hey Jim, you dig that? Maybe we better pull around the block."

"Them? Shit, they don't mean nothin, uniformed cops." Jimmy continued his conversation with the man leaning on the car. B.J. thumbed the pages of his paperback. The two policemen crossed the street to the corner diagonally opposite us and seemed to look at the car.

"Hey Jim," Slick said. Jimmy glanced up at the cops and looked back at his friend.

"In a minute," he said to his friend. "Okay," he said to Slick, "let's move around the block. Shit, you worry about them fuckin uniformed cops."

"Not worried, just careful," Slick said. "I don't worry about nothin with B.J. in the back," he said with a chuckle. He looked into the rear-view mirror at me and said, "Hey B.J., show him your fist." B.J. turned mechanically and made a fist with his right hand, rotating it between us, a huge bulging brown hammer of knuckle and muscle. Slick swung the Eldorado in a lazy right-hand turn. "Some people call that the hand of God," he said, chuckling again.

Jimmy turned around. "You got any questions you want to ask B.J.?" he said.

"Not just now," I said.

"My partner's thing is dope," Jimmy said when we were alone. "You know, duji, smack, scag, tragic-magic. I don't dig the heroin thing personally. Then you got to deal with crazy junkies. Slick and me started on reefer, and I went to coke and he went to scag. Scag is where the most money is. But me, I laid with the other two. I don't sell scag. I just tell Slick to see so-and-so. I don't take care of it. I don't even want to know about it, man. So I got into coke. My clientele is different. No junkies. Like, a two-and-two, that's worth at least ten dollars. It would cost you maybe forty or fifty dollars to coke up yourself for the evening. So you're dealing with some people got some bread. And they don't get strung out snorting. So if they run out, and they don't have any bread, they don't have no habit coming down on them that sends them after your ass."

"That stuff you showed me when we sat out on Riverside Drive," I said, "that wasn't coke, was it?"

Jimmy smiled slightly, an expression that could at once be a smile or a sneer or a snarl, depending upon the circumstances and the words that followed. "No," he said, "that was scag. I just brought it to show you. I thought you'd be interested."

"Jimmy is pretty violent," said a friend who has known him since before he became a hustler. "He is tough as hell. He has to be. It's kind of strange that in some ways he operates more like a pimp—with all that flash and taking all the risks he takes—than a typical dealer. But he has the perfect hustler mentality. He's bright as hell. He's terrific with figures. I try to get him to go into a legitimate business where he could have it both ways—the fast life and a little longer one—like in records maybe. Because he is smart enough and tough enough to run any kind of business. But he'd break a head open. I don't know if he has ever killed anybody, but I think he could."

10

When I first met Jimmy in the summer, he had been dealing cocaine for about a year. His goal then was to lay aside $100,000 by Christmas—five months away—buy a nice house, retire from hustling to run some legitimate business, marry his woman, and raise a family. Hustlers don't live long as hustlers. "I *know* it's not a career," he will say. So far he has not been busted, not since his childhood days, and never for drugs. Many hustlers survive, few make it big, but the dream is there for all. It is, in fact, the dark side of the American Dream.

2

Cocaine: white crystalline powder derived from the coca plant native to the Andes Mountains of South America; a powerful central-nervous-system stimulant that is the least-discussed of the so-called "hard drugs," yet is a staple in the diet of entertainers and the favorite of the drug dealers themselves; the most expensive "high" of them all; the King.

In the illegal drug business, cocaine is sold cut in $10 or $20 capsules (a $20 cap is enough for anything from a three-and-three to a six-and-six, depending upon the snort); teaspoons and tablespoons (tablespoons are "quarters"); "pieces," which are four tablespoons, or about an ounce; parts of "keys" (kilograms, 2.2 pounds) from eighths, quarters, halves, all the way to whole keys of pure cocaine, which cost, in New York, anywhere from $14,000 to $20,000.

A dealer is a pusher with status. The pusher is the lowest level of drug peddler, selling the smallest amounts directly to the users on the street. The dealer sells larger "weights" and has some protective layers of personnel between himself and the street.

For reasons of both money and safety, the dealer tries to move up the ladder. Soon, a dealer always hopes, he will be able to generate more business than his own supplier can accommodate, and then the dealer can jump up a step to deal directly with the man his supplier has been buying from. Each step up means there is another shield between the dealer and the street, and the farther from the street—where carelessness, stupidity, violence, and risk are greatest—the more secure the business. As the dealer rises up the ladder, he buys larger amounts, which enables him to handle a purer quality of cocaine, have greater turnover, and deal with fewer and more responsible people.

As with any other business, advancement is largely a function of ambition, wit, and daring. A dealer may deal easy, at a moderate pace to complement income from other—perhaps legitimate—enterprises, or he may deal hard, high-pressure, running at top speed full time to make it quicker. In either category, the cocaine dealer is not a shopkeeper reliant upon random customers drifting in off the street. The dealer must be a discreet and consistent customer for the man above him. Just so with his own clientele, it must be trustworthy. While there is consignment and credit, it is on a short-term basis, and the terms are harshly enforced. It is a business of huge cash flow, and commits the dealer to a delicate balancing act.

Jimmy deals hard, which means that he invests all he has in product, and then must move it quickly to get his money back. Everybody along the line is pressured to move the product quickly, because cash must flow back up the stream in a hurry. Jimmy doesn't always have product on hand, since he himself must have the cash—or most of it—to buy it. When a good customer wants cocaine, Jimmy, now himself a customer, must make a quick connection for purchase, for if he is unable to provide the right quality of coke quickly enough, he risks losing the customer to another dealer. So he doesn't say he can't get it. In the manner of a true salesman, his pitch is always positive. He'll string you along. He can always get what you want. Sure, get right back to you. Sometimes, rather than admit he can't get it—either because he is short on cash or because his supplier is short on product—he will simply become unavailable, go underground much the same as a threatened debtor, and will surface when he has the product. This, along with a loose-schedule life style and care for security, is why communications with him, as with other dealers up and down the line, are undependable. There are some long nights for dealers and customers alike, while at one end of the line a customer waits hungrily for some snorts of coke, and at the other end the dealer searches anxiously for cash or a supplier with cocaine on hand. Neither cash nor product lies around very long. His skillful manipulation of these elements caused Jimmy to suggest from time to time that I call him the "Juggler."

Dealers keep their records various ways. Jimmy keeps a good bit of his business in his head, some in a pocket notebook, some on scraps of paper tucked into his wallet. First names are listed, and beside each is a dollar figure which is that amount owed to Jimmy. Higher up the line, somebody's book has Jimmy's name listed too, with a dollar figure beside it. "Normal" buying and selling keep him hopping. What jams up the whole system and jeopardizes operations for everybody are delinquent accounts. Debtors, therefore, are punished with sometimes dramatic severity.

"Hey!" Jimmy said. "You know what B.J. can do?" He stepped back against the wall and fanned out his hands, palms down, slowly. "B.J. can stop your heart without even breaking the skin. B.J. can take any part of you and break it in two before you say a word. B.J.—hey, you know what he can do? You're standin there, right? I'm standin here. I'm B.J. Maybe you got a roscoe in your pocket. B.J. can swing his leg all the way up and touch his nose with it. You know what that means? That means his leg can take your head off on the way. And you won't even see it comin. He'll drop a dude so fast, and the dude will hurt so bad he'll wish he had been shot. Listen: I'm pretty good at karate myself.

14

We mess with it sometimes. Me and Slick and B.J. mess with it. And when we do, B.J. will kick my ass and he will kick Slick's ass at the same time."

"It sounds," I said, "like B.J. is a pretty mean fellow."

"It's not that really," Jimmy said, knitting his brow. "Actually B.J. is a very nice guy, very smart, reads. Chicks dig him. I don't know why he's the way he is. I never knew anybody else like him. He just has no emotion. B.J. is solid ice. I pay him $200 a week, plus half of what he collects, and all the jewelry—you know, all these cats down here wear rings and shit.

"Like I'll sell a cat some product on consignment, and we'll set a date for payment, maybe a week or two away. Okay? It's agreed. Coke is expensive, so you deal a lot on consignment. Okay, the date comes, the dude doesn't show. Or maybe he shows and he says, 'Hey man, things are so fuckin tight I just ain't got nothin and my woman's sick,' and so on and so on, and I say okay. I say that's fine. That's cool. I don't need to hear a lot of shit. I'll extend it a bit. Then the cat doesn't show. Maybe he begins hidin and dodgin, but sooner or later we meet, and he starts in about how tight it is and the cops and nothin is happenin in the street and shit and shit and shit, and I say 'Hey!' "

Jimmy stood with feet apart, arms toward me with palms down, eyebrows arched, mouth narrow. "I say, 'Hey! We don't need to talk. We have already talked. I gave you some product. You owe me some money. We set a date, and we extended it because I know that shit can come down. Okay, now I'll extend it again. You will pay me Thursday. Cause if you don't pay me Thursday, you can't pay *me* no more. After Thursday, motherfucker, I don't want to see you. I will not talk to you. After Thursday you do not pay me. You pay B.J.' "

Jimmy swung his right arm in sharply and snapped his fingers. "Hey, you know what that means? You know what

15

it means to pay B.J.? Cause you don't talk to B.J. at all. B.J. comes up to you with his palm out, no questions, no shit, no nothin. And into B.J.'s palm you put the money, all of it. Now you see, if the cat had paid me some of it, you know, kept it straight, I'd give him some time, as long as he keeps coming around. But when you pay B.J. you pay all of it, right then, every penny. So I am tellin this motherfucker, after Thursday you got to pay B.J. You know what? I have seen grown men cry when I told them that. I've seen dudes without an ounce of punk in them actually get tears. They don't want to pay B.J. There just ain't nobody like B.J."

Jimmy shook his head as if it were difficult for himself to comprehend.

The collection starts with ritual staging ("Shit, we learned it from the movies," Jimmy acknowledged one day). When a debtor disappears, he is sought in the bars, perhaps as part of the normal rounds, or even, if the search is more urgent, by patrol. If the three of them go together, Jimmy, who takes himself to be the best shot, will stay just inside the door while B.J. and Slick sweep through the bar to the back to see if the man is there.

"One guy that we knew was a friend of the guy we wanted was sitting at a bar one time and we went up to him," Jimmy said. "Right away he started blubbering, 'I didn't do nothin, I didn't do nothin.' And B.J. had to take his arm and say, 'Cool it, man, get it together. Take it easy. Where's your friend?' And the dude told us"—snap!—"like that. When this stuff is goin on, everybody at the bar turns their heads away. Nobody wants to know nothin."

When the search is completed at a bar, B.J. and Slick walk back to the front and out the door. Jimmy is the last to leave.

"There's this guy in Brooklyn," Jimmy said. "He owed me a lot, you know, for a long time, and we went through the shit and all, and he started hidin. So we went to find him. He lived in an apartment. When we came up the stairs, we heard voices, but when we knocked, this broad opened the door and said there was nobody there. I just pushed the door open and waved her aside with my twenty-five and kicked open the bedroom door. There were four or five cats in there snortin and gettin high and shit. The man wasn't there. So we searched everybody for guns, and then began to look around. I found him standin in the closet very scared.

"So B.J. took the man from the closet and walked him out. I backed out of the bedroom, and before I shut the door I said, 'First thing anybody's gonna meet comin out of here'll be God.' B.J. took the cat to the kitchen, and a couple of teeth came out and so on. The cat was yellin, 'Don't kill me, don't kill me,' which I could dig, you know, cause the dude was terrified, cause B.J. was settin fire to his ass. Then this bitch comes out of the bedroom and she is so scared that she has to go to the bathroom. I let her go, and then for a long time I don't hear anything in there, so I look in. The bitch has climbed out on the fire escape. I haul her back in. She's sobbin and moanin. I had to slap her to make her come around. Cause she figures we're going to kill the dude and then we'll have to kill all the witnesses. But we're cool. We aren't going to kill anyone. We don't need that heat. We come out of there with I guess about nine hundred dollars and some rings. The dude still owes me about five hundred. We'll get that too. He has to pay that to B.J."

Jimmy's workdays are erratic. If there is a pattern, the ordinary workday can be said to begin at about noon, when he primps, makes some phone calls, and leaves his apartment. He will visit half a dozen bars where he makes contacts, or keeps an eye on those making contacts for him. Then he will hit some after-hour drinking spots, and maybe a dice game or two. He will get home by perhaps 6 A.M., or perhaps 10 A.M., or perhaps not at all.

"Jimmy doesn't sleep," a friend told me. "I know he says

he sleeps until about two in the afternoon, but I haven't seen it lately. He is really on the move. He's got so much going on in his head. And the amount of reefer and coke he is consuming in daily use is way beyond the commonplace. I don't know how long he can keep going at this pace."

3

Introduction to Jimmy's world was made gradual and cautious by his understandable reluctance to reveal anything—his car, his apartment, his woman—by which he might later be identified. "I am not," he said, "a retired hustler writing his memoirs." He had to reckon not only with the police but also with nervous associates. "But he's the power source of the operation," a friend told me. "He doesn't really have to ask anybody for permission to do anything." Meetings were always difficult to arrange. Weeks would go by without contact.

For a time we met in his car or mine, or at another person's place. I didn't even have his phone number. He used to have an answering service, but by the time I discovered that, the service had been discontinued. At last a friend gave me his home number and said, "Fuck it. He may be a little angry, but he'll get over it." Jimmy was a little angry, but it broke the ice. And in any case his apartment proved in the long run to be the most convenient and secure of possible meeting places, since he supposed that my accompanying him to his "gangster bars" might get either or both of us shot or at least would damage his credibility in the business.

Jimmy lives in that no-man's-land above central Harlem, just off an avenue, in a neighborhood once splendid, now of mixed races, blessings, and respectability. Our first meeting on his turf was set for 11 A.M., and I was prompt.

In the small entrance hall separated from the lobby by a

door with an electronic lock operated by the tenants, I pushed the button for his apartment. Nothing happened. I pushed it again, and again, and again, and held it, but still there was no responsive buzzing in the door latch. I thought that he could be in deep sleep, or that he could have changed his mind or still be out. I also had some dire thoughts of things that could have gone wrong, or go wrong when I entered. I went out and up the street to a laundromat where there was a pay phone. I called him, and he answered on the second ring. He said that he had not heard the buzzer, but that it occasionally malfunctions. "I'll wait exactly a minute and a half," he said, "and then I'll start buzzing the lock, and I'll just hold it long enough to make sure you get in."

I returned to the ante-lobby, but this time it was not a lonely place. Also locked out now by the faulty system were two elderly well-dressed white ladies standing silently, and two rough-looking teen-age boys muttering in Spanish. One of the boys held a football. All four stood looking at the rows of names and buttons. I pretended to push one of the buttons, and suddenly the doorlatch rasped open and the five of us went into the lobby, a spacious area with ornate walls and columns and mirrors which reminded one of the earlier elegance of upper Harlem. We all boarded the elevator. The boys got off at a lower floor. "I'm glad you came along," one of the elderly ladies then said to me. "We had keys of course, but we didn't want those boys to come in. You just never know in this neighborhood anymore."

"I guess that's so," I said. I pushed the button for the top floor, hoping that the ladies were destined for lower ramparts. They were. I got off at the top, walked down the stairs, and pushed Jimmy's doorbell. I heard him shuffle forth, heard the peephole cover slide open and shut, heard a series of locks and bars sprung, and then was welcomed in.

Jimmy was dressed in a green robe which ended just below his knees, and leather slippers. His Afro was not yet

20

combed, and he yawned and rubbed his eyes. "What's happenin?" he said wearily.

"I'm fine," I said. "How are you?"

"Tired, man, really tired. Just got in a little while ago. Aaaah, yeah."

He motioned for me to go into the living room, and he continued down the hall.

"Be back in a minute," he said.

The living room was in immaculate order, essentially pastels of brown and red, subdued in hue and uncluttered by extravagance. The floor was covered with a thick-pile carpet of deep red—a rug already of some legend to me, for several of his friends had mentioned that when it was new, everyone was required to remove shoes upon entry. Curtains were drawn behind a long brown sofa which faced, on the opposite side of the room, a large color television. Beside the sofa was a Princess-model telephone which, I was later to hear, announced a call by a delicate two-tone chime rather than a traditional ring. Along one wall was an assemblage of high-quality electronic gear, a blend of Sony, KLH, Lear Jet in amplifiers, receivers, tape deck, speakers, turntable. In one corner was a broad velvet lounge chair shaped in an undulant continuum like a gentle wave. Bookshelves along one wall held a few thick hardcover editions of encyclopedia, engineering, black philosophy, and biographies. Under the shelves was a magnificent chess set of translucent stone. A lamp hung from the center of the ceiling, and could be dimmed by a rheostat mounted on the wall. A strand of synthetic vine hung from ceiling to floor behind the lounge chair and was doubly reflected in the two full-length mirrors mounted on closet doors on opposite sides of the room. Above the hi-fi hung a rectangular painting perhaps four feet long whose character was muted brown and red abstraction dominated by straight lines, severe angles, and sharp points.

In a minute Jimmy was back, carrying a rough-textured

21

green ceramic canister about two inches in diameter and three long which was opened by sliding up one curved side, and which held in this case a substantial amount of marijuana that Jimmy called Calif.

"Want a smoke?" he asked. With quick dexterity he rolled four joints, using two Bambú cigarette papers for each, and folding up a millimeter on each end to keep the contents in until lit. He put them on the table. Then he lay back in the lounge chair and carefully pulled his robe together over his knees.

"So," he said, "what's happenin?"

"Why don't we just start at the beginning," I suggested.

"The beginning of what?"

"Well, your life. . . ."

"Oooh, shit. That's going back a l-o-n-g time. Shit. My life? Whew. I guess you could write a whole book about that. But that would take some time."

"Well," I said, groping for openers, "how about the beginning of the week?"

"Yeah, let's see. This is Saturday. So you mean, like, from last Saturday, or from Monday, or . . ."

("He'll probably play with you some," a friend had confided. "He'll be careful and dance around. You might have to be a little patient. But I think he's already made the decision that he trusts you. He's made some checks and so on. But he wants to talk.")

"Why don't we just talk about the last few days," I said. "How've things been going?"

"Mmm. Well, the last few days have been a little bad, man. Some bad shit set me back."

"Is that why you never called on that Sunday, you remember a couple of weeks ago, when we were supposed to meet?"

He pulled his robe together again and smoothed it and stretched.

22

"Yeah, well, some people planned to take me off, planned to bother me. They were going to jam me up. But in preparing to do it, they let a person know, a person that was tight with a broad I know. He ran it to her, and she in turn ran it to me. So when I showed, I showed ready. They made a no-no, and they got caught. So that's why I didn't call you."

"But things are going all right now?" I asked.

"Well, it's slow right now. But it's slow all over, not just slow with me. Slow with everybody. Nobody's got any money. The administration, you know. I guess that sounds weird—think of the President and all, involved with this—but it's real. Money is tight. Money in the street is tight. If it's tight on the street, I *know* what it's like for a nine-to-fiver, you know."

"You mean like me?"

"Well, I don't actually consider you a nine-to-fiver now, doin what you're doin, you know, on your own. But I suspect it's tight with you too."

"And you can feel that, in your business, in the street?"

"Shit yeah. All these poverty programs and whatnot that they had goin on out there, when they're gone, money is tight. Nobody's got cash. If they really checked it out, I think they'd find that the crime rate, stickup-wise, takeoffs, is higher than it was. Everybody's just goin after the dollar. The cost of living is so fuckin high it's retarded, man. Hey, listen to this: My toilet broke. Now, I don't own this fuckin building. I just live here. My toilet broke, toilet thirty-five, forty years old. They replaced it, and wouldn't you know, they increased my rent?

"And then, uh, well, there have been some problems. My partner took a fall, you know, got careless. He just came out of the house half-awake. He had parked his car illegally, blockin a cat's driveway, and the cop rather than tow it away got into it and looked around to see who the car belonged to. And there was some hot shit in there—not dope, but some clothes and shit. So my partner came down and got busted. But that's an illegal search, so he'll beat that. I had to put up a grand for bail, but I'll get it back. Cost me a little for a lawyer and so on."

"Why you?"

"Well, my partner's money situation is a little fucked up. Just now he's got nothin. But shit, I'll get it back. That's what partners are for."

The front door slammed, and Jimmy turned sharply around. "Hey, baby, come here." The girl who came into the room was pretty, with soft features and long black hair and tastefully matched tight slacks and blouse. She had an armload of groceries. "Hey Phyl, I want you to meet Richard. Richard, this is Phyllis."

"Nice to meet you," she said with a smile. I said the same. She walked out to the kitchen, and then called from there, "You-all like chicken?"

Jimmy nodded to me. "Sure," I said.

"Any particular part?" she called.

"Anything's fine," I said.

Jimmy came over and sat next to me on the sofa. "That's my woman," he said in a lowered voice. "That's the woman I'm going to marry, probably when I retire. She's a doll. She's somethin else."

"She is very pretty," I said. "She looks like a sweet girl."

Jimmy smiled. "She can be a fire-breather. And you know what? She is super-square. She comes from the midwest, and her family is super-square, very nice. She doesn't snort, she doesn't smoke, she doesn't drink, she doesn't even swear. But she's smart. College girl. And she can be tough. Don't let her fool you."

Jimmy picked up a joint from the table, straightened out one end which he put into his mouth, and lit it up with a large round table lighter. He breathed in deeply. "Mmmm, aaah, time for breakfast." He took from his robe pocket a

24

little aluminum-foil packet of coke and opened it on the sofa cushion between us. Then he paused and listened to the faint rattle of kitchen noises. Phyl came out of the kitchen and passed the living room without looking in. Jimmy shielded the packet with his hand. "Mm-mm. She sees me do it, and she doesn't dig that. She thinks it's degrading. She can be a fire-breather." When she returned to the kitchen, Jimmy creased a matchbook cover and scooped up a two-and-two. "Aaaah," he said, tilting his head back and rubbing his hand over his nose. "That's good blow. A good two-and-two, a good reefer. Yeah." He relit his joint, took a deep drag, then held the lighted tip under his nose to take in the escaping smoke. He held his breath, then sniffed a few times to clear his nose.

"Hey, you remember my brother, who just came back from Vietnam?" he said. "Stinking motherfucker got busted the other day, for receiving stolen property. But that's just a fuck-up. It cost me some dough, but he'll beat it on the facts. Some dude tried to unload some stuff, you know. Cat walks up to you with some hot shit. You don't necessarily know it's stolen. He's in the process of purchasing some shit when the police show, and the guy splits and leaves all the merchandise right there. They chased the other guy, but they busted my brother. But the cat that owned the store saw the dude that stole the shit, and he knew it wasn't my brother. So I told the guy I'd either return the goods or give him cash value—about $170 worth of shit. So he's not going to press charges."

"That's kind of rough for your brother," I said, "just back from the war."

Jimmy chuckled. "Shit, my brother wants to be into hustling. He has a brother that's a hustler, so he wants to be a hustler. I'd like to see him be a nine-to-fiver, you know. I'm talking about being a full-time nine-to-fiver, doing a job. I would not like to see him get croaked. I would not like to see him doin part of his life in the penitentiary. Plus he's

25

dumb. He don't know nothin about the street, cause he's only twenty. What the fuck are you gonna learn in twenty years? Out of those twenty years, he's probably had thirty days' experience in the street as a hustler. And you can't use the experiences of a child as a jumping-off point, you know, a foundation-type thing for hustling. You got to get your lumps and bumps. Me telling you is not enough. Cause if he'd have listened to me, he wouldn't have got caught buying that hot full-of-shit stuff, you know. Like, I'm telling him, don't be a hustler. Be a nine-to-fiver. And he looks at me and he sees my diamonds and he sees my Eldorado, and he looks at what I've got and he says, 'What the fuck are you tellin me?' He looks at what I've got, but he doesn't see the blood, sweat, and tears that go into it, you know. He never sees that."

"But hustling is a kick for you, isn't it?" I asked.

"Oh, well, like I enjoy it in a way. But it's not a big kick. It's survival. It's like, how could I go back to a job making a hundred dollars a week? But you see, the chances of my brother making it nine-to-five are much greater than the chances of me making it nine-to-five. He's got more education, he's younger. . . ."

"Food is ready," Phyl called from the kitchen.

Pancakes were stacked on the three plates, along with breasts of chicken, deep-fried and crisp. Phyl poured orange juice and milk into tall glasses. "Jimmy likes his orange juice strained," she said. "I already put butter on the pancakes." Jimmy downed a glass of milk, and she poured another.

"Hey Jim," she said, "are we going to the pet shop this afternoon?"

"Mmm, maybe," he said, taking a big bite of pancakes. "She wants a dog," he said to me.

"You going to get one?" I asked.

26

"Yeah, I think so. You know what? I'd really like a big dog, a German shepherd, but not in an apartment. But when we get a house, I want a big German shepherd for the yard. He'll stay out there. I don't want him in the house. But we'll get a little dog for the house. Just keep him off the furniture."

"You know what?" Phyl said to me. "I'd really like to have a cat, but Jimmy doesn't like cats."

"If you brought a cat in here," he said, "you know what I'd do with it."

"Oh, Jimmy exaggerates so much," she said, continuing to me. "We had a cat once, and he even used to let it sleep on the foot of the bed."

Jimmy arched his eyebrows. "And what happened to that cat?" he said.

Phyl smiled shyly. "He took it to the pet shop."

Jimmy smirked. "Cat peed in my chair," he said.

"Well, the cat was in *heat* Jimmy," she said.

"Why don't you like cats?" I asked Jimmy.

"You can't do anything with them," he said, "can't train them. You put a cat on your lap and you pet it four or five times and it gets an attitude, you know, starts wigglin and wants to get down. A small dog would be good in here, just so it doesn't jump up and break my chess set."

Phyl put another round of chicken breasts on our plates. "Would you like some more pancakes?" she asked me. "Jimmy only eats three pancakes. Always three." She shook her head, and then added in a manner more protective than critical, "He eats crazy anyway. Now he's got an ulcer, a peptic ulcer, right? And he waits until six or seven o'clock in the evening to eat, then he doesn't eat again. And he wonders why his stomach bothers him so."

Jimmy finished his orange juice, and then leaned back chuckling. "Hey Phyl, you know what's the very best thing for my stomach, the very best thing?"

"What?"

"A two-and-two. Then I'm feeling just fine."

He laughed, and Phyl shook her head. "Oh Jim," she said as she took the plates away.

Jimmy was pacing the living room. "Yeah, couple weeks ago I had a nice piece of cash laid away. Not a whole hell of a lot. Seven or eight grand. So, let's see. My partner's fall cost me about three grand, of which a grand was bail and I will get back. And then there were some other expenses incurred at that time, you know, the cop was on the ball, and circumstances prevailed. He had a pistol on him when he took the fall, you know, he was dirty. Shit, it costs. But what my partner owes me is money in the bank anyway. I bought him a car, cause he was down, for about six grand. He'll pay me back sometime. Oh yeah, and then something happened on Thursday. This dude owed my man a piece of cash, $2,200 or $2,300 I think it was, nice piece of cash. Most of it was mine. He had to come up with the bread. But it became apparent that he wasn't going to come up with the bread—not because he couldn't, because, shit, then we would have waited, cause we wanted the bread. But the dude *wasn't* going to pay. So he went off a roof. So I lost. . . ."

"Off a roof?"

"Yeah."

"Well, a high roof, or a little roof, or, I mean, was he hurt bad or what?"

Jimmy smirked. "Roofs are usually high, hmmm? And he don't hurt no more."

"So all the money you had put away is gone."

"It'll come back."

He was still pacing, musing. "Like today, I'll get my shit together, get a shower, get dressed, and get out of here. I got to visit five or six places. I got to see a few people. Hey,

28

one dude I'm gonna croak. Gonna bust his ass. Owes me eight hundred dollars. Supposed to pay last week. He's been hidin. I hate somebody tries to fool with me. Saw him yesterday, told him I had to have my money. I'm gonna set fire to his ass. He'll have it. He doesn't have the heart *not* to.

"Yeah, I'll hit those five, six spots, get some money. I'm owed about five hundred dollars to fifteen hundred each. I'm not gonna get all of it. But each one, say, I'll get two, three hundred dollars. Then I'll go out there and see who's got to get paid, who's doin what, what's comin off. Few specific spots, bars. I'll put in X amount of time. I got to get *movin*."

Abruptly he stopped pacing, and rubbed his chin. "What should I wear? What to wear, what to wear—that's always the hassle."

4

I parked my car in front of Jimmy's at the appointed hour and waited for him. Soon he came, walking with a girl and carrying an armload of groceries. The girl got into his car, and he put the groceries in after her, then walked ahead to my car and slid in beside me.

"Ain't she a number?" he said. "She's a total freak. What you got?"

I handed him a six-by-ten-inch black book trimmed in gold with CASH in gold letters on the cover. It was an ordinary ledger book, except that the owner had added alphabetical thumb-tabs, and the entries pertained to dealing drugs on a fairly large scale. It contained notes, first names, balances for sales of "Red Leb" (perhaps marijuana) for $37.50 an ounce, pounds of hashish selling for $770, "Reds" (perhaps Seconal) at $175 per thousand, ounces of "Napalese H" (perhaps hashish) at $75 each, and so on. "Doug" owed $2,000; "Stan" was in for $15,100; "Dave" had brought his balance down from $14,625 to $1,876 at last entry.

"Whew!" Jimmy said as he thumbed slowly through the pages. "Where'd you get this?"

"I came upon it," I said, "by accident."

Jimmy calculated silently, trying to deduce what each item was.

"You can never be exactly sure with some of these entries," he said, "because each dealer usually has his own kind of code, symbols he uses for himself. But I can tell you one thing: Some dude is sick, man, without this book. He is really sick. You better just throw it away. Better not let the cat who owns it find out you got it. And it better not be lying in your car if you get stopped by the PO-lice."

Jimmy glanced up at a helmeted policeman cruising by on his motor scooter, then nonchalantly continued his perusal of the ledger. He noticed my nervousness. "Fuckin uniformed cop ain't gonna bother you *or* me. He's got no right to be botherin us in this car."

He snapped the book shut and handed it to me. "I really haven't got the time to rap now. I'd like to be with *her* for a hot minute," he said, nodding his head back toward his car, "and also I think I got to get out to the stash tonight."

The dealer's status, reflected in his ledger, is supported in his "stash," which is, aside from the dealer himself, the heart of the operation. Primarily, the stash is where the drugs and processing equipment are cached, where the cut is milled in and the drugs are packaged for sale. Since drugs are not "saved up" like money, the size of the stash indicates not savings or thrift, but the more important flow of drugs through the dealer's business. Additionally, the stash is a hidden storage depot for armament and even cash, since banks are not appropriate repository for this money. "I know guys with pillowcases full of cash," Jimmy once told me. "So much cash they actually don't know where to put it." So when he has some extra thousands he wants to put aside, the money joins the extra pistols, ammunition, and the drugs themselves at the stash.

As important as building the stash is protecting it, for it is the stash that holds enough evidence to get Jimmy and Slick killed or sent to prison. Ordinarily, nobody but Jimmy, Slick, and perhaps a few associates who help with the milling is permitted near the stash, or even to know its location.

They don't keep their stash at home. "If they bust me at my place," Jimmy explained, "and there's some weight around, that is a heavy bust, and I go to prison. But if they bust me at home now, what do they find? A reefer? A little personal shit? That's nothin. A suspended sentence at the most."

They have their stash in an apartment building outside the city, rather than in a more convenient Harlem location. "Cause the neighborhood's the thing," Jimmy said. "Like, around here or down in Greenwich Village, the cops just have to have *that* much"—showing a pinch—"suspicion, and they'll bust the door down. But I keep my stash in a fly neighborhood, a white, respectable, high-priced neighborhood where the cops don't go bustin down any door just because they feel like it. They don't hassle people out there. A girl lives there, a very respectable girl with a very respectable job. And when I go out there I'm s-o-o straight, dress well, drive a nice car, always polite, just visiting, like I was somebody's very nice boyfriend."

When he buys product, he usually takes it directly to the stash. When he has a sale lined up, he returns to the stash to mill. He visits the stash about three times a week.

At 1:30 one morning, Jimmy called. "Meet me at three o'clock at the corner of East 125th Street and First Avenue," he said. "We'll take a ride."

I drove down the nearly deserted street at 2:30. The air was warm and still. Some hookers were still strolling, lonely, their eyes professionally attracted to my car. A few men sat in doorways. At the end of 125th Street I backed in among some warehouses and waited. Very close to on time, Slick's Eldorado appeared and parked. Seconds behind came Jimmy's Eldorado. Jimmy got out. He was wearing a white applejack cap, a bright red-and-blue flower-patterned shirt tailored tight to his body, dark slim trousers, and white shoes. He looked around casually; then,

32

with short, quick steps, came over to my car. His shirt was open at the neck, and his gold coke spoon dangled and flashed in the streetlights like a spinning lure. He nodded and said, "Let's go."

Slick was in the back seat. He was wearing an apple-jack cap and bell-bottom trousers. As usual, he greeted me politely and welcomed me to the trip. Jimmy's eyes were narrow, and he was quiet and smiling confidently.

"You look like you feel good," I said.

"I'm all coked up," he said.

Steering with his left hand, his right on the armrest near his pants pocket which held his .25 automatic, Jimmy started heading slowly west along 125th, then abruptly wheeled into a U-turn, tires squealing, and sped back east, through the intersection, under the bridge ramp, and onto the East Side Highway headed north. His eyes were on the rear-view mirror. He slowed down to fifty, plugged a tape of Stevie Wonder into the stereo, and leaned back, bathed in the music which came from front and rear speakers. Then he reached into his shirt pocket and took out joints of marijuana and passed them around. Slick and Jimmy hummed along with the music. After a couple of miles, driving in the middle of three northbound lanes, Jimmy began to watch a car upon which we were gaining. The car was in the right lane, and three men were in it.

"Check that," Slick said from the back seat.

"Right," Jimmy said. He slowed to maintain a position just off the left-rear fender of the other car, until that car went off at an exit. Jimmy sped up slightly and watched the mirror, for from that exit a car could proceed through an intersection and reenter the highway almost immediately.

"Damn, move your head, Slick," Jimmy said irritably. Slick leaned away from the rear window. The other car did not return to the highway.

"They looked sho-nuff," Slick said.

33

"Mmmm," Jimmy said.

"Good day?" I asked, after a time.

"Shit yeah," Jimmy said. "Made nine hundred dollars today. Tomorrow I got a sale worth maybe forty-five hundred. That's the way it can go sometimes. Then some days you just want to lay up and fuck off. That's when you begin to lose money, or if you get busted or something."

We drove several miles, with the music and the smoke filling the car. Then Jimmy swung the car off at an exit, slowly at first, and then once on the curving ramp he sped up so that the car leaned and the tires whined. He watched the mirror. Then he drove slowly through some residential streets, making a turn here and there. Finally, on a quiet tree-lined street he pulled into the rear parking lot of a dignified brick apartment building. We sat for a few seconds, then got out and went to the basement door. Jimmy fumbled for his key, and we went in and boarded the elevator. First Jimmy pushed the button for the third floor, then for five, seven, and ten. He looked cocky as hell.

We got off at three and went to 3B and went in. The lights were on, and Jimmy told Slick and me to go into the living room, while he went into the bedroom for some brief mumbled conversation with the girl who lived there.

The stash was about to be moved, and cardboard cartons filled with personal belongings, dishes, books, clothes were stacked against the walls.

"Would you care for a soft drink?" Slick asked, pouring a Pepsi for himself.

Jimmy and the girl came in, he with the short-stepping swagger he walks with sometimes, she, sleepy-eyed, in a quilted white bathrobe, wearing the tolerant smile of a hostess upon whom guests are suddenly thrust.

The hunger from grass was upon us, and the girl went to the kitchen to make sandwiches. Jimmy went to a closet and hauled out a large shiny blue metal trunk. "Chick's in a mood, man," he whispered as he set the trunk down in the middle of the living-room floor. He took out a ring of what appeared to be dozens of keys, fumbled with them, dropped them, and then began to laugh. "Slick, I got so many keys it's retarded, man." Finally he opened the pad- lock and the trunk lock. He was on his knees as he lifted the lid and laid it back all the way open. Then he sat back on his haunches and waved his hand at the trunk. "Well," he said to me, "that's what it looks like in real life."

There were plastic containers of the type used to store food in refrigerators, packages of aluminum foil, plastic bags, bundles of rubber bands, measuring spoons, a box of Bambú cigarette papers from Spain, a box of .25-caliber bullets, sifters, a strainer made from a nylon stocking stretched over a metal clothes hanger.

"Hey, Slick, here's the spoon I been looking for. Damn."

There was a balance scale of the type used by druggists, that measured amounts from one to one thousand grams. There were plastic jars of lactose and dextrose, used in cutting coke and heroin, and quinine for the heroin.

Jimmy opened a two-quart plastic container that was empty except for a white film of powder lining its sides, and he held it up for me to sniff the bitter fumes of cut heroin. Then he handed it to Slick.

"Look what I found," he said. "I just handed you forty dollars' worth of stuff you didn't know you had."

"Lucky if it's twenty dollars' worth," Slick answered. He tore off the front of a matchbook cover and began meticu- lously scraping the insides of the container. "But it's a gift, no shit."

The girl brought out plates with sandwiches, thick hot fried ham steak with lettuce and tomato on toast, and glasses of Pepsi. We ate while Jimmy continued spreading the contents of the trunk on the floor. The girl leaned against the wall, saying little, wearily coquettish once in a while with Jimmy, smiling at Slick's teasing about how well we ate and whether she'd been into the trunk.

"Let me show you the place," Jimmy said. We left the living room, went through the narrow kitchen, where we replenished our sodas, and walked down the hall to the bedroom, a pastel cavern of draperies, ruffles, frills, and soft lamps, all dominated by a triple-size bed. "Dig this room," Jimmy said. "It's a home away from home. Hey, this place costs me a lot more than my own apartment."

Slick came in, carefully carrying the round lid to the plastic container he had been scraping. On the lid was a little mound of heroin.

"Hey, Jim, nice to find," he said, holding it up.

"Always nice to find something you haven't counted on," Jimmy said as he left the room.

Slick put the lid on a table and played with the powder with the matchbook cover.

"How much would that be worth on the street?" I asked.

He began separating the mound into tiny segments. "Each of these would be about a two-dollar bag, so let's see." He formed some more tiny hills. "I guess it'd be about thirty-five dollars, if I was going to sell it." He creased the matchbook cover and deftly scooped up one of the little piles and snorted it, then snorted another. "But I don't think I'm going to sell it." He inhaled several sharp breaths to draw in the tiny bits which clung to nose hairs. "Yeah, some good scag, on top of some good reefer."

"Do you think Jimmy's reefer is good?" I asked.

"Hooo, yeah. Hey, I wouldn't smoke three of those Jimmy has, not in a row. They would take my head away."

We went back into the living room. Slick picked up a magazine.

"Jim, will you dig this. They writin about *us,* man. No shit. Has to be us, cause dig this title: *How Sex Keeps You Slim.*" He reached down to show Jimmy the issue of *Cos-*

mopolitan and traced his finger under that line on the cover. "Has to be about us, man, or at least about me." He pulled his shirt up and tapped his lean waist and rib cage. "Look at that. Not an ounce of fat. Has to be about me, man."

"They said slim, not skinny," Jimmy said. He was on his knees, surrounded now by a dramatic still life which he had at last completed to his satisfaction by positioning his .25 automatic in the middle of it. "That's the whole scene, man," he said. "That's really the whole scene."

Slick turned on the radio, to a newscast. The news was about a march for women's liberation.

"You dig that?" Jimmy said, laughing. "You hear that?" He went over and playfully tapped the girl on the shoulder. "You hear that shit? All you got to do is make 'em eligible for the draft, and that will be the end of *that* shit."

The girl smiled, and Slick leaned back on the sofa and closed his eyes and chuckled. Jimmy turned the radio off. He was up with the coke energy, and he paced, touching things, moving his arms, catching reflections of himself in the mirror.

"Jim," Slick said. "We got to mill soon, no shit. We got to get out of here before the weekend. We *got* to."

"Yeah, things a little low."

"And I got to pick up some quinine, man." Slick turned to me. "With scag you use something like milk sugar to stretch it. Then you use quinine to boost it. Quinine isn't really to cut it. Quinine gets it quicker to the man. With that quinine in there, boom! Just as they squeeze it they feel it. It gives scag a rush."

Jimmy walked out to the kitchen to talk to the girl. Slick sipped a soda. "See," he said, "for coke you don't need a whole big operation out here. But like when we mill my stuff, we hire maybe six or eight guys, you know, guys be-

37

tween jobs or with nothing to do, guys we know, and they come out here and sit at the table there and package stuff. They make a dollar a rubber band. Fifteen two-dollar bags, that's a half of scag. It's bound together with a rubber band. The cats measure it out with a spoon into the bags, you know, and they get a dollar for each half. Sometimes we work a real long day, maybe twelve or fifteen hours, to mill up."

Jimmy came back in and went over to the door and squinted at the one-way peephole.

"How's business?" I asked Slick.

"All right. You know, people owe, they pay. Hey Jim, dig this: Remember that cat I had to find? Cat that was hidin? I saw him yesterday, and he said he'd pay me today, you know, without question. So today he didn't come around, so I came around instead. I knock and the cat opens up and there I am, you know. So he says, 'Oh man, hey, glad to see you because I was just comin over.' So I say, 'Well, that's just fine because I have saved you the trip.' " Slick laughed and skinned Jimmy's palms.

Jimmy put on a record of the Supremes. "I think it best we have a little, uh, diversion if we gonna talk." For a few seconds he moved to the music and snapped his fingers; then he paced, arms and shoulders moving, eyes steely. "You see, the stuff that comes out of here is always good. But that's the trick. See, Slick's business is with junkies, and what every junkie really wants to do is croak. That's what he wants. A good O.D. is what every single junkie is really after. I'm not bull-shitting. Listen, here's the story: Some junkie croaks in the Bronx, right? He takes an O.D. Okay, right away all the junkies start talking, 'Hey, did you hear that so-and-so O.D.'d in the Bronx? Oh yeah? Where'd he cop?' See, right away they want to know where he got his stuff, because they figure if the cat O.D.'d, it must have been some superfly duji. So right away they all

38

want to know where he copped. 'Cat copped from Shorty. Oh yeah?' And boom! Everybody's off—tcheeew!—to find Shorty and get some of that same shit that gave the cat an O.D. in the Bronx. Cause an O.D., that's where it's at, man. Cause an O.D. is the most fantastic high of all. Like you can give a cat some bags of super-fantastic dope, and he shoots up and is noddin and dreamin and so high he can't even raise his arms. And you say to him, ain't that fantastic dope? And the cat says, 'Yeah, but it could have been better.' *Better!* Do you dig what the cat is sayin? He is right on the edge, on the high of his life, barely alive, and he is saying it could have been better. Better means O.D., man, O.D. That's what the cat wants. He may not *put* it that way, like he talks about gettin higher and higher. But the cat knows that higher is O.D., and that's what he wants. That's what they all want."

This is really Slick's game, heroin, but Slick is smiling with closed eyes, legs stretched out and crossed in front of him, humming with the music and saying nothing. His eyes, occasionally open, are streaked with red. He is on a heroin high and drowsy and happy. Jimmy is on a coke high, and he is pacing and swaggering and talking, sharp and quick.

"You see," Jimmy continued, "you got to be careful about where you cop your stuff. Like it isn't just because somebody will cheat you—because to cheat you is to get shot. But different cats sell different strengths, or different quality. Like up in the South Bronx the dope is generally weaker, the junkies aren't so tough. In South Harlem the stuff is stronger. So a junkie is used to shootin up three bags, say, for a good high in the South Bronx, and then he comes down to Harlem and cops and shoots up three bags of some stuff that may be as strong as four or five bags of the stuff he is used to. That's an O.D., man. The very best superfine dope I have heard of will stand a twelve, you know, twelve pieces of cut to one piece of dope. Everybody prays for a twelve. Very fine dope may be on a nine. Usually good dope will take a six. Now, if you're used to stuff that's on a six, and you get some stuff that's on a four—cut only four times—and you shoot the same amount you're used to, that's an O.D. Or if you been copping some dope that's put on a six, and then you go to another cat and cop some superfine dope that could take a nine, but it's actually on a six, you shoot the same amount—tcheew!—an O.D."

Jimmy looked over at Slick. "Look at your bad self, noddin."

Slick smiled with closed eyes. "Not noddin, man, listenin. Ain't nothin *to* do but listen when you're talkin."

Jimmy lit up another joint. "Now you wonder why would somebody sell you more value for the same price? Maybe he's just dumb. But when I'm milling up, I always put in a little extra, just give them a little extra. That keeps the quality up, that keeps business up, that keeps your reputation up. You start shortin people and you lose business or you get shot. People always lookin for better quality. They come to the man with the quality. It's the same with my product. I don't deal in dope. I don't dig that whole junkie scene. My clientele is different. People don't O.D. on coke. But they want quality. Like the very best superfine coke can take a four. But mostly the good stuff can take a three for the street. Now when I say my stuff can take a three, I mean it can *take* a three. I don't fuck you around. I sell you stuff guaranteed on a three, and you will *like* it on a three."

"How come you don't have a big pile of coke here," I said, "ready to sell?"

"Cause you can't just have it lying around—unless it's pure. And to be buying it pure, you can't be buying eighths, you can't be buying halves, you got to be buying kilos, which I can't do yet. You see, you don't be pre-cuttin coke. It doesn't last as long. Cut eats coke up, eats up the potency. I could take an eighth of pure coke home for two weeks, say, and it'd still be good. I take an eighth of cut coke home, and in a week it gets kind of, you know, weak. So you don't cut coke until you're ready to sell it. You cut it as the orders come in. So the way to have some weight at your stash is to be buying pure, and you build it up. Same with scag, except that scag will stay longer. And you don't use quinine with coke like you do with scag. Quinine will eat up the coke. Quinine gives heroin a rush, but there's other things that give coke a rush and don't eat up the coke."

"Like what?"

Jimmy smiled mischievously. "Like other things. See, you cut coke with lactose or dextrose, or both. I add a little of another thing which makes my coke superfly."

"What other thing?"

He smiled again. "Call it mysterious. There are certain things you don't want *nobody* to know. Got to protect my formula. Let's leave it mysterious. What I do is, I buy lactose and dextrose by the case, twelve containers to a case, and I usually use them together as cut. You get them in these plastic quart bottles." He picked up two opaque factory-labeled containers. "I mix them together. Then you got to sift them. You sift the cut to get the pure sugar out of it, the sweetness out. Then you sift the coke to get the biggest lumps out—although I leave in some of the rocks to show the quality. Then you weigh up the cut and the coke on the scale, then mix it together in a plastic jar."

"That's all?"

Jimmy raised his eyebrows.

"I mean, it doesn't sound very complicated."

Jimmy looked at me through narrowed eyes and rubbed the tip of his nose. "Nothin is complicated," he said slowly, "if you know what you're doin. Now, some cats fuck around trying to be chemists. Good coke will numb your tongue, numb your nose. That's a way you can tell if it's good.

41

Cats trying to be chemists will fuck around adding procaine and benzocaine and all those freezing agents to make
the coke *seem* better. But you can taste the difference, because good coke doesn't have a freeze. Good coke has a
numb. Procaine won't get you high. Benzocaine won't get
you high. They're freezing agents, deadening agents. They'll
freeze your mouth up. If you had an open cut and it was
hurting you and you rubbed that shit on it it would freeze
it, but it won't get you high. Nothing get you as high as
good clean coke, sniffing it or shooting it. That's why you
deal with somebody reliable, so you won't get burned."

Jimmy gave Slick a playful kick. "Hey, that's some
reefer. Ain't that some reefer?"

"Oooh, yeah," Slick said, stretching his legs.

"Hey, you remember when we brought that reefer in?"
Jimmy asked. "Hey, that was a trip. Me and Slick brought
reefer in, how many times? Three times? We brought in
a hundred pounds. That's for friends, you know, and personal use mainly. But I wouldn't do that today. They are
gettin tough. Hey Slick, you hear that today, about the
big bust in Paris, maybe the biggest in the world? Two guys
and stuff worth something like seventeen million dollars.
You see that on television? Two suitcases full of scag.
Wow!"

I asked him if a bust like that would be felt on the
street.

"Whew, is that felt on the street? You better believe that
bust is felt. Everybody starts holdin on tight to their stuff"
—he clasped his arms around himself—"and they start
looking around to see what's going to happen. Nobody
knows how far it will go, you know, how far down the busts
will go, or where the supply will be cut off. Price might go
up. Everybody's gonna look things over and see what's
happening before they sell anything."

He paced the center of the room. "But I'm gonna bring

some more reefer in. And I got me a plan to bring in some coke, I mean a whole lot of coke. I got me a plan to go to Ecuador and bring me in a hundred keys of coke."

"Shee-iit," Slick said, getting up off the sofa, laughing. "*If* you can bring it in. You got a *plan*."

Jimmy looked at him stony-faced. "You don't think I can do it?"

"I just think that's a awful big plan," Slick said, chuckling still.

"I'll do it. I really want to go to Ecuador."

At 5 A.M. Jimmy said it was time to leave. Slick looked out the peephole, and Jimmy gave the girl a hug while Slick and I went to the elevator.

"That's a good job," Slick said, "being a writer. You got a son?"

"Son and daughter."

"Yeah, well, what do they think about it? I mean, you know, are they aware of your situation?"

"What do you mean?"

Slick looked away and rubbed his lip and tugged his ear, then looked back at me. "I mean, you know, like, uh, if something happens, you know, like if something happens to us, some shit when you're with us, like you can't just, uh, disappear. Like what I mean is, do they know the dangers?"

"Oh, I guess so. Journalists are always taking little risks here and there, and they don't get hurt often."

"Yeah, well, that's an interesting business."

Jimmy joined us, and we rode the elevator down. I was pondering Slick's solicitousness when we emerged into the dimly floodlit parking lot. Straight ahead of us, directly behind Jimmy's Eldorado by a few yards, was now another Cadillac, black, with both front doors open. Inside were three shadowed faces, white, with sunglasses on. I stopped short, but Jimmy and Slick kept on walking evenly, their

43

eyes fixed on the other car. So I followed. Slick opened the right-hand door of Jimmy's car and got into the back seat. I slid into the front. Then Jimmy opened his door and got in.

"Dig it, dig it, dig it," Slick said softly.

"Mmm," Jimmy said as he started the engine and backed toward the other car. Then he spun the wheel with a finger and drove calmly out of the lot and down the quiet street. The other car remained in the lot.

Jimmy wound his way back to the highway. Nobody talked for a while. Slick snorted some heroin in the back seat, and Jimmy passed out reefers. He set the automatic Cruise Control at fifty miles per hour, took his foot off the accelerator, and leaned back in the seat. He sighed. "Man could just go to sleep," he said. "I don't want to get a speeding ticket."

"What was that back there?" I asked.

"What? That in the parking lot? Nothin. Well, it wasn't no fuckin narco bulls, I knew that. Once I touched the car door I knew that, because they never would have let me get into the car. First thing that came to my mind was not the police, but a takeoff or something. Didn't you see the two dudes with the broad in the back seat? Yeah, that was a broad in the back. Two dudes and a broad. For a minute I thought it might be a takeoff, but I guess they were waitin for somebody, or they had some little thing goin or what-not."

"How could you be so sure they weren't after you?"

"Oh, there are things you look for. Like those guys weren't there when we arrived, and they didn't follow us out there, cause that would have been impossible. No one followed the car. I think I'm an expert at spotting that. You know, the rate of speed I was traveling, the moves that were made. If anybody was following, I would have seen them. Have to. Because of the turns that were made it would

44

be impossible to follow and I not know it. Like coming off that rotary turn—remember how I speeded up? If somebody was behind me, they would have had to keep me in sight. It's not hard to spot somebody following you if you're looking for it. They have to be able to see your car. And if you can see my car, shit, I can see your car—unless you're in a plane, like a helicopter, and that's unreal. So, they weren't there when we arrived. And when we came down, well, you make a habit of doing certain things when you come out of the stash. Like you have your roscoe in your hand, not your pocket."

Jimmy sighed and took a slow drag on the joint, then held the lighted tip under his nostrils and inhaled that smoke. "Oh yeah," he said. "That's a good stash. You know, one time I was out there somebody even busted into my car and stole some tapes. I called the cops. Damn right! I called the fuckin PO-lice to come and check it out. It turned out that some of the neighbors had seen the cat that did it, and they caught him. A white cat. Can you dig it? I was the *victim*." He chuckled and took another drag. "Good spot for a stash. But we got an even better one coming up, right, Slick?" He looked at Slick in the rear-view mirror.

"Wheew," Slick said, red-eyed and drowsy, "all I can think about is how happy I am I don't have to drive."

There was little traffic on the highway, but Jimmy watched each car that passed without turning his head.

"What would happen if you got stopped right now," I said, "for speeding or something?"

"Right now? They'd ask for my license and registration. I'd give them my license and registration, which are in order, which are always in order."

"What if they want to search your car?"

"I tell them it's illegal and I won't permit it."

"What if they do it anyway?"

"They push it and it comes to a shootout. Cause if they search my car, I go to prison. Open the glove compartment."

In the glove compartment was a brown paper bag rolled up.

"Now close the glove compartment," he said, smiling cockily.

"Back there in the parking lot," I said, "what would have happened if they had come out of that car flashing badges?"

"Badges and guns?" He chuckled. "I don't know, but it sure would have woke up the neighborhood."

Jimmy backed his car in beside mine. I got out, and he rolled down his window. "Check with you later," he said as I walked to my car. At that instant I caught a glimpse of two policemen, up on the overhead bridge ramp, leaning on the railing looking down at us.

"Holy shit," I whispered to Jimmy.

He smiled and nodded. "Just keep movin," he said.

5

Recently two doctors, on one of those countless "drug-abuse" seminars on television, concluded that cocaine had "lost its status" among "drug addicts" and that it had been supplanted by "other more effective, less dangerous stimulants" such as the amphetamines.

Perhaps they got their information from a basic medical reference work, *The Pharmacological Basis of Therapeutics,* which states flatly, "Cocaine abuse is now uncommon in Western countries." Or perhaps they were confused by other sources. It *is* true that cocaine has lost its status in the *medical* world. It was perhaps the first, and for many years around the turn of the century the best, local anesthetic, used primarily in dentistry and for ills and surgery connected with the eye, ear, nose, and throat. Today in this country it has almost entirely been replaced by more effective and less toxic local anesthetics, the first of which was procaine (under the trade name of Novocain), which was synthesized in 1905.

But illegal cocaine use, on the other hand, is increasing by gigantic leaps. In 1970, for the first time amounts of illegal cocaine seized by the federal government exceeded seizures of heroin. The Bureau of Narcotics and Dangerous Drugs (part of the Justice Department) reports that in 1970, 267.92 kilograms of coke were seized by agents—a 500 percent increase over amounts seized in 1969, and a 1,200 percent increase in four years. Over the same four-year period, seizures of heroin have approximately doubled, to 221.79 kilos for 1970.

Some of this increase is due, of course, to increased vigilance on the part of law-enforcement authorities. But federal officials have also been acknowledging since the latter 1960's that illicit traffic in cocaine is increasing. "It seems," a Narcotics Bureau chief told me, "that cocaine is simply being used a lot more every year." The rock-drug culture accounts for much of the increased usage, but there is as well a stunningly broad group of well-known and well-heeled public personalities—particularly in the entertainment field—who are regular users of cocaine.

Illicit use of the drug is severely penalized. Users are subject to the same sentences as those of heroin. Peddlers get up to fifteen years and fines of up to $25,000. And some state laws are even tougher. New York, for example, gives up to life imprisonment. Given the combination of such widespread use and harsh penalties, one might expect sophistication from the experts. But the federal government, while showing increasing concern about the drug, is performing no experimentation on its effects. Unfortunately, cocaine, compared to heroin and marijuana, remains ominously mysterious to the public.

Several varieties of the brown or green coca bush, reaching heights of between six and eighteen feet, grow both wild and cultivated on the Amazonian side of the Andes at elevations of from four to six thousand feet. It is cultivated as well in the Indies, Ceylon, India, and parts of Africa.

Some sources trace use of the leaf as a stimulant back fourteen centuries, when the Incas worshiped it, probably because it gave the chewer increased endurance. Chewing coca leaves is still common among the Andean Indians. According to the Justice Department, the total world need for coca leaves to produce legal cocaine for medical use, or flavoring substances for beverages (such as Coca-Cola), ranges between two and five hundred tons. Yet statistics from Bolivia and Peru alone indicate an estimated annual yield of twelve to fifteen thousand tons—most of which is chewed by native Indians. It is estimated that eight million people still chew the coca leaf.

In a revealing résumé on cocaine and the coca plant, John T. Maher, a Narcotics Bureau official, wrote: "The fidelity of the present day Indians to coca is due to superstitious ideas retained from ancient times and the necessity to survive 'modern' living in South America. The Indian whose meager fare consists of maize, dried meat, and potatoes relies on coca to sustain his strength, in many cases for mere survival. Without the physical fortification of coca, he would not perform the grueling work required in the mines."

Laws against ingestion of the plant go back centuries also. Christian missionaries saw the devil in the leaf, and four hundred years ago colonialist governments passed laws against chewing coca. Subsequent to imposition of the laws, the use of coca was perceived to increase, rather than the opposite. This result, Maher ingenuously surmises, was "a natural consequence in defiance of prohibitive laws."

Today, importation of leaves and manufacture of cocaine are tightly controlled under federal narcotics laws. Only two companies, the Stepan Chemical Company and Merck & Company, are licensed by the Justice Department to import coca leaves to make cocaine. In 1969, according to Justice Department figures, 268,679 kilos of leaves were imported to produce 1,184 kilos of cocaine—and 884 kilos of that were exported, primarily to European countries where cocaine is more widely used than here as an anesthetic.

For cocaine manufacture, leaves are picked by hand and dried slowly in the sun. Cocaine, produced either as an alkaloid powder or a more water-soluble hydrochloride, re-

49

sults from a complex process of washing and percolating the dried, crushed leaves with solvents and other chemicals. According to the Narcotics Bureau, clandestine laboratories in South America—especially in Peru and Bolivia—are the source of nearly all illegal cocaine. In powdered form, the drug is smuggled into the United States primarily through Miami and New York.

In general, discussion of the "drug problem" tends to be rabid and uninformed. Talk on cocaine is no exception. Cogent answers to the salient questions—How dangerous is cocaine? Is it addictive? How widespread is its use?—are scarce. And there is much authoritative contradiction.

One major problem has been, of course, that talk about "drugs" has lumped together everything from marijuana to heroin, as if central generalizations could be made (the blows struck by Harry Anslinger and his Federal Narcotics Bureau in the 1930's were powerful and have had lasting effect), although lately it has become acceptable to treat marijuana separately and somewhat more lightly. But cocaine and heroin are still almost universally united under the topic of "hard drugs" (a vague term used to imply serious danger) or "narcotics," despite the fact that they are medically and pharmacologically opposites. Indiana University sociology professor Alfred R. Lindesmith wrote in *The Addict and the Law* (1965) that the opiates (opium, morphine, heroin) "are so completely different from such substances as marijuana and cocaine that they cannot intelligently be discussed together with them."

First of all, one must define "addiction," and these days, in the matter of drugs, one defines it to taste. Generally now (one suspects in order to include marijuana, which has become increasingly difficult to call "addicting"), two types of addiction are described, one physical and one psychological. In the former, a test is usually whether the body develops a "tolerance" for the drug, requiring increasing dosage to achieve the same effect. That works for heroin or morphine, but killed it for grass, since authorities now wonder whether heavy users of marijuana might actually need *decreasing* amounts ("reverse tolerance") for the same "high."

Psychological "addiction" or "dependency," however, is a much more malleable term, and can be spread over any habit which is difficult to kick, from drinking coffee every morning, to picking one's nose unnecessarily, to cocaine. It can even be applied to a habit one simply *prefers* not to kick. By and large—risking a hoary generalization—people take drugs because they want to, whatever deeper spirits and humors are involved. In the case of heroin, whether one likes the drug or not, it is physically addicting and damaging to the body. What about cocaine?

In the thick fourth edition (1970) of *The Pharmacological Basis of Therapeutics* the authors set forth another definition: "If the term *addiction* has meaning, then in terms of the compulsion to continue use, the degree to which a drug pervades the life of the user, the tendency to relapse following withdrawal, the compulsive user of amphetamines or cocaine is an addict." Such reasoning is circular, for a "compulsive user" would be one irresistibly drawn to the drug even against his will, ipso facto an addict. And such a definition excludes, then, those users who want to take cocaine.

On page 295 of this book is the statement: "There is some question whether tolerance develops to cocaine," followed by data to support this uncertainty. On page 381 is the statement: "Both addiction and tolerance can result from the continued use of cocaine."

The Dispensatory of the United States of America, another thick volume, is a basic reference work for pharmacists. In its twenty-fifth edition, under the heading "Addiction," are the following statements: "The habitual use of cocaine as a narcotic stimulant [a curious juxtaposition in a

51

pharmaceutical work, since a narcotic—such as the opiates —is a 'down,' a depressant to the senses, a sedative, while a stimulant is precisely the opposite] is a problem of sociological importance. . . . The cocaine habit is not only one of the most seductive but also one of the most rapidly injurious and difficult of eradication of all drug habits. . . . There is a psychic rather than physiological dependence on the drug."

It seems to me that the last statement deflates the one before it.

Earl Ubell, science editor of WCBS-TV in New York, prepared and narrated in the fall of 1970 a prize-winning series of reports called *Drugs: A to Z.* In it he stated: "Heroin is not the most addicting drug; cocaine takes that prize." That remark was followed on a later broadcast with: "Cocaine *may* [italics mine] be the most addicting drug known." He said a few moments later: "The usual dependence of heroin does not follow cocaine addiction. When the drug is stopped, the individual does not feel the same withdrawal symptoms as he would with heroin. But if he does stop the drug, the craving for it is excruciating [unlike heroin?] and he soon falls into a deep state of fatigue and mental despondency, so deep in fact as to sometimes cause suicide."

A search for answers is frustrating. One source says cocaine is addicting, another says that it is not; one says that cocaine abuse is widespread, another that it is not. Cocaine users perceive such terms as "cause suicide" as hyperbole. The potential drug user who seriously wishes to know the extent of the dangers, or who is at least willing to listen, quickly discovers that the information peddled doesn't check out. So he is likely to throw out the wheat with the chaff and believe nothing.

Here is a synopsis of the effects of cocaine from clinical sources: Cocaine is one of the strongest central-nervous-system stimulants known. As an anesthetic, it blocks conduction of nerve impulses when applied directly to tissues. It does not anesthetize unbroken skin, but is immediately effective on, for example, mucous membranes. It is ineffective when taken by mouth—being rapidly detoxified by the liver—but highly effective on the central nervous system when injected into the bloodstream.

The stimulant properties first affect the cortex—the higher brain centers—making the user mentally and physically restless and active. It is a relatively short-acting drug, and for a brief time mental alertness may be heightened, reflexes quickened, and physical strength and stamina increased—though the latter may be an illusion due to the disguising of fatigue. It is a highly pyrogenic drug, causing body temperature to rise or fluctuate, and breathing may become shallow. As with the amphetamines, appetite generally lessens, and with repeated doses, the user can go without sleep for several days. In short, the central nervous system is hyperactive. While the user is "up," he may experience feelings of supreme confidence and power. In some it produces aggressive behavior or confusion. The user may become obsessed with detail.

Withdrawal from heavy cocaine use may be severe, producing extreme fatigue, depression, paranoia, and even psychosis. In acute cocaine poisoning, there is nausea and hallucination—the sense that small things are crawling over one's body. Death may result from respiratory arrest, or, if cocaine is injected into the bloodstream, from cardiac failure due to direct toxic action on the heart.

There is no disagreement that cocaine is a powerful and toxic drug. But perhaps one problem with clinical discussion of drugs is that, however accurate, it seems unrelated to "normal" life. For example, a clinical analysis of the effects of alcohol is fearsome. But the nonalcoholic drinker may find it difficult to relate his alcohol to that of the laboratory

—or the hospital. The same is true in the matter of cocaine. The terms "paranoia," "aggressive behavior," and "hallucination" (death is a concomitant of an overdose of so many things, from cyanide to salt) seem not to relate to what might be called "normal" use of cocaine—and in some respectable circles cocaine is used as "normally" as alcohol is in others. The effects of, say, ten snorts in an evening vary with the individual—just as do the effects of alcohol, marijuana, and coffee. Socially, such as at a party, cocaine users are typically alert, active, more confident, and more "open" or communicative (talkative people become more talkative). This is about the opposite of what happens at a pot party, where marijuana smokers tend to withdraw, and more resembles the early hours of a drinking party. Cocaine effects differ from those of alcohol in that users tend to stay alert and communicative as long as they continue snorting, whereas the activities of drinkers tend to deteriorate and become slow.

As the quality of a cocaine "high" is an individual matter, so is that of the "crash"—the descent from the "high." One may, after heavy use of cocaine for a day or two, feel profoundly fatigued for a couple of days after, and depressed as well (the two discomforts ordinarily go together anyway). But, as with an alcoholic hangover, a "normal" user of cocaine can usually predict his level of suffering, and whether you dominate it or it dominates you is largely a matter of individual disposition or personal will. University of Rochester psychology professor Dr. Helen H. Nowlis wrote in *Drugs on the College Campus* (1969): "It appears that no known drug has effects which in and of themselves compel a normal individual to use them repeatedly. In other words, as with alcohol, we have to discover and identify for each drug the social and psychological factors which deter or facilitate repetitive use and dependence."

Unlike the amphetamines—which ironically may turn

54

out to be more dangerous and habit-forming than cocaine—pure cocaine cannot be obtained by a doctor's prescription. In terms of dealing with "hard drugs," this is an important fact. A druggist's normal mark-up for profit on cocaine, were he permitted to sell it to private citizens, would put the price at something like $50 an ounce. A respectable druggist I know, who hasn't been presented a prescription for cocaine solution in ten years (the last was for a patient suffering hemorrhoidal bleeding), was the other day offered $1,000 for an ounce—about the going rate for pure in the underworld.

"I-I-I-eeeaaam, gettin the spirit, mm-mm-mm, in the dark. I'm gettin the speeeriiit, oh yeah, in the dark. People movin, really groovin, just gettin the spirit, mm-mm, in the dark. . . ."

Aretha Franklin, what are you singing to me? Voice sliding in and out of that dark, tones insinuating, climbing my backbone and fluttering through my hair, voice sliding free up and around, such sweet pain. "Gettin the spirit, oh yeah, in the dark."

I don't know how long I have been watching the ants. On my elbows on the kitchen floor, watching their intricate scuttling across two feet of tile to the ant trap, a little round flat can with poison inside. Mindless beasts, I suppose, crawling and telling others somehow, and the others come out and zigzag across the floor to the ant trap to snatch a tiny piece of that white powder in their mandibles and dash back across the floor and disappear down the hole to their nest. Ants "getting the spirit, mmm-mmm, in the dark."

I am comfortable on my elbows, watching the eager death march just below my nose. I understand the powder, but I don't understand the ants. Running across the floor day and night in a frantic pageant of instinct: the drive to live which will cause them to die. Into that little red-and-white ant trap with the cover that they can't perceive which says "Keep away from children and household pets." And they carry delicious specks back to their nests, just as their bodies made in three simple sections make them do.

"If you feel like dancing, get up and let's start dancing. Gettin the spirit, mmm-mmm . . ."

It is raining in the suburbs, a warm fall rain dripping from the feathery branches of the pine tree, slipping down the colored-glass panel in the window. Leaves swirl up in the wind, an army of hunched gnomes marching away from me, away together in the wind, and then springing up to do an insane dance in the air behind the tree. The spirit dazes the nasal nerves and whams into the back of your head and makes your eyes glow and your mind hum and your arms move and sends sweat slithering down from your armpits. Red candles, red book, silver watch, blue pen, black clock, brown ants. People should see colors like that always, and hear the beauty of a pure sound that pops from a single guitar string and expands and hangs in the air for a long time if undisturbed.

There are all kinds of the spirit. Didn't Claude Brown stand before that elevated white judge and think now judge if I could get a little of the spirit to you, then you'd understand why we have trouble that causes you problems. We could *rap,* judge. And didn't that rock singer try to get another kind of the spirit into President Nixon's tea, so he could sip the spirit, just once?

Hey God, do you know about the spirit? Are you on your elbows up there?

And the ants are getting the spirit. One of the ants has lost the trail. A hysterical ant waving his antennae. No grace here, ant! Oh no, you don't have to push it to the ants. They *want* the spirit too. And they got to get it to the queen.

"Tell me sister, how do you feel? Tell me brother brother brother, how do you feel . . . ?"

56

We will pay for this tomorrow, ants, and perhaps the day after tomorrow. But then, everything has its price. Yours is that you will all go down there together to the nest, with the queen, and you will crinkle up and O.D. And then you won't be bothering me in my kitchen anymore. One dares not think too deeply about the scheme of things.

"Put your hands on your hips, cover your eyes, and move it, with the spirit, mmm-mmm. Are you gettin the spirit, mmm-mmm, are you gettin it in the dark, mmm-mmm . . . ?"

Jimmy leaned back in the sofa and took from his robe pocket a tightly rolled dollar bill and carefully opened it up. "This," he said, "is absolutely pure, worth maybe four or five hundred dollars. It's my personal. See those rocks in there? That means it's supergood. And it has a very medicinal smell, right? That's how good coke smells."

He teased the powder with his gold coke spoon. "I don't usually prefer it pure, but sometimes I come across a little, you know. I got some in the other room that's cut a half. That actually tastes better to me. But, aaah, that's there, and this is here, so . . ."

He snorted a two-and-two. "Hear those things dropping back in the paper? That's rocks. Don't snort the rocks. You got to be careful not to snort the rocks, because one can lodge in your nostril and burn the membrane and hurt you."

"Somebody told me that pure coke would make you sick," I said, "give you a nosebleed, headache, upset stomach, and so on."

"Who told you that? Somebody who doesn't really know. You talkin about that drugstore coke? You can't go snortin that pharmaceutical shit. It's so strong it will wreck you—whew! But, yeah, this here can make you a little sick, depending on how much you take. Enough of it will give you diarrhea, that's for sure. Actually I like it better with a little cut in it, gives it a more pleasant hit. So usually when I come across a little pure like this I will add maybe a little less than a half to it."

"What do you do with the rocks," I asked, "just throw them away?"

Jimmy snapped his head up. "Do *what?* Hey, hold it! I hope nobody's throwin rocks away. The rocks are pure coke. Look here." He took out an aluminum-foil packet that had been passed on to him by a friend for a critique. He took a tiny single snort, and then sat pensively for a few seconds. "Hmmm, not too bad. But now, it could be better. See all those rocks in there? Okay." He folded the packet flat, and using the bottom of his lighter, pressed the package firmly, rubbing the heel of the lighter back and forth. Then he reopened the packet. "See? No more rocks. Now . . ." He took another tiny snort. "Much better coke. You just leave the rocks in there to show the quality. But there comes a time to mash 'em up, and that's when you are gonna snort 'em."

"How much do you snort in a day?"

"Well, if my woman is here, not much at all, cause she doesn't dig it. But I snort coke seven days a week. I'll snort a two-and-two just to open my eyes in the morning. Shit, I might snort a quarter—that's a tablespoon, a hundred and fifty dollars' worth of coke—in a day. Yeah, I guess that's a lot."

"So you're high just about all the time."

"Not necessarily." He stretched. "Oooh, yeah, tired all the time. I do a lot of runnin, you know. I haven't been to bed for a couple days. I'll sleep tonight maybe four or five hours."

"It's coke, isn't it, that keeps you going like that?"

"Shit no, man, that's all the sleep I need anyway. Lot of people get along with four hours a night. That's all I got when I was a nine-to-fiver. It's all in *here,*" he said, tapping his head.

58

"Are you telling me you're really not hooked on coke?"

"Hey," he said, cocking his head and arching his eyebrows, "there ain't no such thing. I've had it when I wanted it for a long time—I snorted my first coke when I was twelve. I don't think *I can* get hooked on anything. Cause when I want to stop, I stop—even if I been up a long time, cause I don't like for my body to *force* me to take it. So I stop, clean my system out, heal my nose up."

"You *do* stop?"

"Sure, I stop sometimes. I stopped about, oh, let's see, in the summer, for about a month, six weeks. Nothin wrong, just wanted to clean my system out. Phyl got on me, you know."

"Can she tell when you're high?"

"No, I don't think she can just look at me and tell. I don't change too tough."

"I can tell," I said.

"Yeah, well"—he smiled—"that's you. I don't watch myself too close around you." He examined his knuckles. "This may seem strange to you, but when I don't take coke I'm actually rather bashful." He rubbed his nose. "I can tell when I need to stop snortin. I'll be on it heavy, you know, snorting a quarter a day, and it gets to a point where you put your finger in your nose and get blood. Or my system doesn't feel quite right. I don't get the effect I should from it. Sometimes my speech might even get a little slurred. These are warning signs to me. See, if I get too high, I get dangerous. I get mean, hot-tempered. That is dangerous. Maybe some pissy-ass dude at the bar says some little thing I don't like. Usually I would just wave him away, you know, 'Come on, man, get away from me, don't bother me.' But if I have too much coke, I might fight the dude. Shit like that gets you in trouble. So when I begin to notice these things, I just get all coked up, have a good sleep, and stay off it a day or two. Doesn't bother me."

"And you don't feel depressed or anything, not like withdrawal?"

"No, man, it's all in *here*"—tap, tap. "Now, the reason I coke up and then go to sleep is so that when I come down, I do it while I'm sleepin. And anyway, so what if you feel a little tired? So what if you feel a little depressed? That's just the way it is. I don't let that *bother* me. Fuck it, you know, I can stand a little discomfort. You get to know your shit. You know when to stop and when to go. And you control it, man, don't let no drug control *you*. A *man* can do anything he wants. Now of course if you go to mixing things, like alcohol, that's something else again. Then maybe you get depressed and down and shit. I don't drink. You know why? Cause I get nasty and mean when I drink—like with too much coke—and when you get nasty and mean you make mistakes. I used to drink—shit yeah!—in the service we used to drink every night. And every night fight some dude. Every morning wake up with bumps and bruises. Can't be fuckin around that way in this business. So I don't drink."

"With so many other things to take," I said, "so many other ways to get high, it surprises me that so many people take coke at those prices."

"What other ways to get high? Scag will kill you. Pills are dangerous, they fuck you up internally. Occasionally it's nice, it's different—I have sometimes mixed a little amphetamine with coke—but a regular thing on pills? Fuck you around! Amphetamines give you gallstones and shit. Acid can leave you a RE-tard, man, a moron. Acid can wreck you the worst. I might take a quarter tab maybe once a month, that's all."

"When you take acid, do you just lay up and trip for a day?"

"Shit no. I can work with it. One of the best days I ever had I was trippin. You remember that day I told you I made thirty-four hundred dollars? I was trippin. And it was jumpin off like *that*"—snap!—"You know"—snap—everything just"—snap. "Oh man, it was jumping off good for me. But you got to be careful with acid. Now, there's hash, but good hash is hard to come by. So that leaves grass. You see, you don't really have much of a choice. Best high in the world for me is coke and reefer. Coke is an up, and reefer is a down. They work well together. Snort a two-and-two, a three-and-three, and smoke a joint—aaaah! Or better still, good coke and good hashy—aaah, that's a boss thing, man."

"But not everybody can snort coke," I said, "not if you're going to spend fifty dollars in an evening just on that."

"That's true, unless you got long dough. If you bought half a quarter of something good, cost you seventy-five dollars. Now, you take half a quarter that costs you seventy-five dollars and put a half on it, cut it another half, that gives you three-quarters of a tablespoon, right? And it's good. You got a blow for Friday, Saturday, and Sunday. You got a blow for the weekend for you and your woman. That's a nice amount of coke, for somebody that's a snort, you know. That's about a ten-and-ten a day for two people. But what happens is that when you snort coke you get open, and you want more. You want to keep that high going, and you keep it going. You can snort up easy forty dollars' worth in an evening. I just had a two-and-two a half-hour ago. That's at least ten dollars' worth of blow, probably more with that quality. I don't feel that coke now, it's on the way out. So okay, I'm ready for another two-and-two. That's twenty dollars. So if you're the average person, you will do it usually when you're ready to go out. You're all dressed and ready to go, and you get high. You take some with you, and you might halfway through the evening go into the men's room and take another two-and-two and keep your thing up. Now, how long you stay high depends upon the snort and the quality of it. On the average I got something that's on a one for my personal. Snort up say a three-and-three, might last you an hour or an hour and a half. Now, two twenty-dollar caps could probably keep you nice for an evening. Then if you got a broad that digs coke, it costs you eighty dollars. But you can't expect an hour-and-a-half high on a two-and-two commercial. If you really want to get coked up and nice, you got to take a three-and-three or a four-and-four. Then in a half-hour or so take another one-and-one, and keep doing that to keep the high nice, cordin to how you like it. Some people might like to come all the way down, and then hit another three-and-three to shoot back up there. Cordin to what you like. But it costs to keep a coke high for an evening."

In the course of the conversation we had moved to the bedroom, and Jimmy was pawing through his clothes rack, bringing out one outfit after another—suits of leather and velvet from France and Spain, silks and satins, pastels and deep colors, white and black, glossy and mat—spreading each outfit over the bed, rubbing his chin, putting one outfit after another back on the rack. Ensembles were shuffled, changed, analyzed, criticized, abandoned. He stared down at a yellow cotton sweater-shirt and brown trousers and a furry brown applejack cap, and shook his head and put it all back.

"Yeah, it's boss, the thing I snort," he said. "But my *partner!* He snorts like he breathes. That's why he can't hold on to no coke. He likes to mix 'em, dope and coke, speed. My partner, if he has coke, he won't use as much scag. He's a high-getter, just digs being high. See, everybody that sells dope uses coke. If they use scag, they're junkies. The lower the level, the more prone they are to use scag."

"How is Slick doing?"

Jimmy shrugged and frowned. "He's got to get his shit together. It could be that he's into it a little heavy." He tilted his head and looked at me. "Could be that he's gettin a little chippie on again. And that could mean that he's movin a little slow, thinkin a little slow."

"He's very thin," I said.

"Yeah. He's always been thin, always *be* thin. His teeth are bad from being a junkie as a kid. Shootin drugs takes all the calcium out your body. It wrecks you. I've seen pictures of him as a teen-ager. His teeth were fine. Until he started shootin up dope and shit. But then he kicked it."

"You ever take scag?"

"I have," he said. He pulled up his sleeve and traced his finger over half a dozen dark spots above the inside of his elbow. "When the situation of my moods was just a certain way, not just depressed, but a whole lot of things together. Some very bad shit was coming down in my personal life three, four years ago. I was on it for a couple weeks, just, you know, really flying." He let his head loll forward on his chest and his arms dangle loosely. "Like that. But I'd never let anybody on the street see me like that. I didn't have no Jones. It is a *fantastic* high, scag is. But you know why I don't use it? It makes me puke, every time. I don't dig that."

"You ever shoot coke?"

"Yeah. I do it sometimes. Mix it with water. You get superhigh, much faster, it lasts longer, and it's much more dangerous. It's *very* habit-forming."

"The books on the subject say an injection of coke lasts just a few minutes."

"They do, huh? Well, that's interesting."

"You say that shooting it up is addicting?"

"Well, maybe it's not a habit like a scag habit. It's a dependency. It's psychosomatic."

"Maybe," I suggested, "it's not addicting in the sense that you don't have to increase the dosage all the time."

"Yeah, maybe that's so." He turned away from the bed to face me, and extended his left arm, pulling up the sleeve. He traced a finger along the large vein above the wrist. "But

I know cats that are strung out on coke, man, cats that have large tracks along here. Man, they have *tracks*. And they don't shoot nothin but coke. Scag you can mainline or you can skin off. Coke you can't skin. You must hit the vein or you don't get nothin, it's waste.

"Shit yeah, I've tried them all, man, mostly because it's to my benefit in this business to know how everything works."

"Did you hear about the seventy-four-year-old guy that died the other day," I asked, "the guy who had been a heroin addict since about the age of twenty?"

Jimmy chuckled. "No, I didn't. But, well, he lived a nice life, man, lengthwise. Seventy-four. Whew! That's older than a whole lot of folks workin nine to five. But then, like I said, I believe a *man* can do anything he wants to do."

"Even an addict?"

"Damn right. Got to know when to say no." He chuckled. "Even to *you*, you know."

The phone chimed. He answered, mumbled some words, then put his hand tightly over the mouthpiece. "Hey Richard, you want to meet a sho-nuff killer?"

"Sure."

He put his mouth back to the phone. "Sure, come on by. Somebody here I'd like you to meet."

6

On one bright fall day, when *The New York Times* proclaimed the arrest of "the number-one pusher of drugs in Harlem" and the smashing of his "$1 million cocaine smuggling ring," I stopped by Jimmy's apartment to see how that might affect his operation.

Jimmy rubbed a swollen knee, which he said had been damaged in a recent collision with the chin of a recalcitrant debtor. "Hurts," he said, bending it slowly and listening to it crackle.

The newspaper story, quoting the U.S. attorney, declared that the man had been arrested for conspiring to import a kilogram of pure cocaine from Ecuador and Colombia. Jimmy scoffed at the news. "Shiiit, every dude they bust got to be the biggest pusher in Harlem, the biggest this, the biggest that. That's how they tell themselves they're gettin somewhere. A key, that's what they arrested him for? Shit. I stopped by to cop today, and my man's got eleven keys lined up. I've seen him with sixteen keys. And he's not the biggest there is."

I had come to share the sense that official valuations on official efforts are capricious, as in the matter of drug seizures, for example. The particular kilo of cocaine we were discussing had been valued at $600,000 by police, though Jimmy couldn't figure it to be worth more than $250,000, even broken into the smallest—most expensive—street denominations. In another instance, a U.S. attorney, in announcing the breaking of a cocaine-smuggling ring, put a "wholesale value" of $30,000 on a kilo. When fifty-four pounds of cocaine were seized at Kennedy Airport in New York, customs officials estimated its worth at between seven and ten million dollars—roughly between $27,000 and $39,000 a key. When a group of South Americans was convicted of smuggling in eighty-eight pounds of cocaine, the "retail value" was set at "more than $4 million," or more than $100,000 a key.

"How much do you have on hand?" I asked Jimmy.

"I got a quarter of a key coming off today, when we're finished. I'm selling a quarter of a key today—worth about forty-five hundred—people from Jersey. Usually I try to keep an average of a quarter-key. Go down sometimes to an eighth, or maybe a little lower than an eighth, half an eighth. Then I get panic-stricken, get some more. I don't *need* to have any more than that on hand. At any time I can call my man, four in the morning, and say I want half a key. Shit, he'll get it to me within a couple hours. A key would take a lot less time probably. If I built up to say five keys, then I got to worry about the stash, got to worry about the stickup man. Now, if the police break in and bust me with a quarter-key, how much is that going to cost me? The difference is if they bust me with five keys, that's life in prison, man."

I knew, though, that Jimmy was hungry for bankrolling. Building the stash and the business takes financing, which may come either directly from business profits—the slow way; or from investments—the quicker way. Here the invisibility of the ghetto dweller is a mixed blessing for the hustler. On the one hand it allows Jimmy to deal more or less openly in cocaine. On the other hand it prohibits normal types of outside financing, such as from banking houses. Commonly the bankrolling may come from another hustler, perhaps further advanced or even "retired," who spots a man like Jimmy on the way up and invests some quick-gain capital in him. It is, to be sure, high-risk capital.

Two of Jimmy's prominent concerns formed a paradox: He desperately wanted the business to grow, while at the same time he worried about living well in the eyes of the Internal Revenue Service. The problem is that the invisibility of the ghetto is not to be trusted. There are those hustlers who have never worked, never filed income-tax returns, never filled out government forms, and thus never, in the nation's official eyes, existed. But over Jimmy's ghetto invisibility is a revealing shadow cast by the fact that he has worked in the past and paid taxes. An investigator would notice that Jimmy maintains a life style unsupportable by unemployment. So there were, at that time, his strange dual quests for big investors in his cocaine hustle on the one hand, and a separate legitimate business cover or W-2 form on the other. That led to at least one investment from the "straight" world.

"I wouldn't give him a regular paystub," a businessman told me, "but he's been after me for some bankrolling. Finally I invested a little bit, a thousand dollars, in his thing, just to help him out more than anything else, and to get him off my back. But who knows? Maybe he'll make me some money."

So now I asked Jimmy, "If somebody gave you twenty thousand dollars today, what would you do with it?"

He smiled. "Okay, twenty grand today? Sure, I'd invest it in myself. I'd invest it in coke. Twenty grand? I'd get a key and a half. But you know how much that's worth? A key of coke costs you, let's say, fourteen thousand. You know how much you can make with it? Forty, fifty thousand dollars in a week, or two, with ease. Now, the very best coke can take a four—you can cut it four times. Commercial coke on the street has usually been cut three times. I can't buy coke that will take a three. Best I can get might take a two and a half. Cause you got to be buying pure coke to get it to take a three. You got to be buying a key to get it pure. Now, with twenty G's I would buy pure coke. I would have to go higher than my guy. He would charge me more than I would be willing to pay. There's a few places where they don't sell a half a key or a quarter-key. The least they would sell would be a key. So I would purchase on that level. But after I purchase on that level, I would come back to this same level I'm on now and deal.

"In other words, I would not buy a key for fourteen thousand dollars and put it on a one and sell it double the money at twenty-eight thousand. That's no money, doubling my money. When I could take a key that was worth fourteen thousand and turn it into forty thousand by selling eighths, pieces—you dig it? The lower you sell, the more you make. So I'd sell it on the same level that I'm on now, cause that's what I sell now, eighths, pieces, every now and then a quarter of a key. There's always more money to be made at the lower level. The money is bigger, but the turnover is slower and the risk is greater. The smaller you deal, the more people you might see. That's dangerous. Here's a man sees two people a week, sells a key apiece, makes X amount of dollars. Now, each one of these cats takes their key and sees three cats. And each one of those three cats sees five people. More risk, but the money becomes greater."

I interrupted this tale of Going to St. Ives to remark that it seemed academic, because he *was* patently trying to deal bigger and bigger, precisely to make more money.

"I'm only saying," he continued, "that the smaller the amount, the more you cut it for the market. You think I would sell fifty dollars' worth of coke and put it on a *two*? In other words, if you buy an eighth, you get a one-and-a-half, say—that's how much more you can cut it. If you buy two pieces, which is half an eighth, you get it on a one. You buy one piece, which is a quarter of an eighth, you get it on a half. That means that you can only cut it another half time. If you buy a twenty-dollar spoon of coke you can't do nothin but snort it. Coke will only take so much whackin. It may be good coke, but it's whacked to the bone by the time you get a twenty-dollar spoon. Cause you're spending such a little bit you can't look for no room. The more money you spend, the more room you look for.

"What you do is, when you have a key of pure coke, you put it on a one usually, and you sell it for top shelf. Actually you're selling two keys, because you've cut it once. Now, if I bought a key for fourteen thousand, I could sell eighths for twenty-three hundred dollars and guarantee a three. And people would eat that hard-rock coke. Oh man, they'd eat that up alive. It wouldn't last no time. It'd be gone. So what I would do is cop big and sell back on the same level as now, taking some of the risk for the bigger bread, cause I can move it fast. Last time you were here I had just copped, right? Okay, I copped today, and I've got to cop again by tomorrow. I'll have a couple of pieces left, that's all. But to talk about being able to cop big—you got to have some long dough. Got to have a backer."

Jimmy started out of the living room, then turned back. "Hey, I haven't really shown you around." He motioned for me to follow.

In the pattern which never varied, everything in the apartment was in its proper place. Clothes were hung away, magazines carefully overlapped on the tables, ashtrays emptied. In passing, I peeked into the bathroom, which was soft and furry in pastels with fluffy covers on the bottles. We went down the hall into the bedroom. The bed was covered by a bright yellow spread. At the head of the bed were four small square leather pillows, each of a different hide and color. Price tags still on each read "$20." "You probably won't see any white cats with pillows like these," Jimmy said with a devilish grin, "because who's gonna go out and spend eighty dollars for four little pillows? I paid fifteen dollars for the four of them."

There was a movie camera on a tripod, hi-fi speakers mounted on the wall. On one wall there were crossed fencing foils. "Yeah, I like to fence." The bookshelves, sparely weighted, had a few nicely bound volumes of technical engineering works, racial philosophy, and reference books. Dominating the shelves were memorabilia. There was a university drinking mug. "I went there for a while, just sitting in on some classes, you know." Propped up against the mug was an envelope, already torn open. He took it down and handed it to me. It had the return address of a professional football team. "They invited me to a tryout," he said. "Don't you know about that?"

"No," I said.

"Yeah, well, I was invited to training camp. We'll talk about that later."

He went over to the dresser and opened the top drawer. "You've seen this, haven't you?" He handed me a .25-caliber Browning automatic.

"I guess so," I said.

"Well, it could have been that one, or it could have been this one," he said, handing me another. "But there's something you haven't seen, cause I just got it." He opened the clothes closet and crouched down and reached far back into a corner, rummaged with his hand, and pulled out a black holster containing a huge .357 Magnum revolver which I recognized as such because I had, a few days before, been given instruction in its use by a bear-conscious scoutmaster on a camping trip.

"Three-fifty-seven Magnum," I said.

He raised his eyebrows and tilted his head in recognition

of my knowledge. "Yeah," he said, "but you know what for?"

"It could be for bears," I said.

"Bears, and other animals," he said.

"Well, it's too big to carry around, right?" I said.

"Right."

"So I guess I could imagine it only for a shoot-out type thing, when it was all or nothing."

"Yup. I'll keep it at the stash."

He handed it to me. I aimed it with two hands, as I had been instructed by the scoutmaster.

"Why you holdin it with two hands?"

"Because of the kick," I said, "to hold it down when it fires so it won't take your head off."

He snorted and took the gun back, extended his arm and sighted, his large strong hand firmly controlling the heavy weapon. Muscles and sinews rippled under the brown skin of his forearm. "It's got a kick, all right," he said, "but you got to know how to use it. It's not much different from the forty-five I used to carry in the Air Force."

"The Air Force?"

"Yeah. We'll talk about that too." He smiled a little. "We got a lot of things to talk about."

He went back to the closet and replaced the holster, and then brought out an attaché case. While he was doing that, my eye was attracted to a large painting over the bed. It had the same characteristics as the one in the living room, soft browns and reds and yellows in disciplined straight lines and points and angles. It seemed to have an overall ominous tone belied by its subject, which was an abstraction of fishermen pulling their nets toward the water.

"Same guy did this one that did the one in the living room, right?" I said, pointing to the painting.

"Yup."

"Who?"

"Me."

"You?"

"Yup. I paint when I got time. But I never have any time anymore. It's like with that Lear Jet portable radio in the living room? I bought it for the beach, but I never get to the beach anymore. I painted these a while ago."

"Did you ever have any instruction?"

"Shit no. It's not hard. Just sit down and do it. They're water colors. Maybe oil is harder. I guess that one in the living room took me about forty hours. I was high, you know, really flying on coke and reefer. Actually I really did it because at the time I couldn't afford to buy the superfly thing I really wanted for my wall."

He snapped open the attaché case. It was a portable drug mill, with bags and strainers and foil and measuring spoons. He took out a cigarette case and opened it. "See those little capsules? Each one holds about twenty dollars' worth of coke. The red tabs are acid, you know, LSD. Acid is fantastic. I love it. Lot of people are scared of it, have bad trips. But that's because dumb fuckers take a whole tab, which is crazy. I take a quarter, then it's nice. Just take a razor blade and cut a tab into quarters. I do that maybe once a month. It's beautiful. Hey, you know what I want to do sometime? I want to paint on an acid high. Wow! I want to do that someday. On a coke high or a reefer high, I control the high. But on an acid high, I let it control *me*. Wheeew! I wonder what I would paint."

He took two joints from the cigarette case and snapped it shut. From the attaché case he took a paring knife and a small plastic bag of cocaine. He opened the plastic bag and teased the powder with the tip of the knife. The light of the room flickered off the cocaine crystals. He sifted through the powder and tapped at a few small hard lumps with the knife. "See those? See those rocks? The rocks are pure. They got to be sifted down. When you see rocks like that you know the quality." He picked up a tiny bit of coke on the tip of the knife, put it to his nostrils, and snorted it. He repeated it for the other nostril, and closed his eyes for a second. "This little bag is worth about $350," he said, replacing it in the case. He put the case away. "I got to get some more, and get movin.'"

"You're not discouraged at all, are you?" I said.

"About what?"

"Well, you been hustling a year, and still you don't have anything."

"Sure I have," he said without hesitation. "Everything in this house is paid for. Don't owe any money on my car. I have nothing else to buy." He opened the closet door and drew his arm along the rack of impressive clothes. "My woman's wardrobe is fly, my wardrobe is together. It's true that I don't have as much as I would like to have cashwise. But I think as far as material things go I have everything I want—or everything I wanted. Only thing I have to do now is go up on my cash."

"What about that?"

"Oh, it's coming. I feel it going up."

"You told me you made an average of five or six grand a week," I said, "and you don't pay taxes. Where does it go?"

"Yeah," he sighed, "where does it go? When you make that much cash, though, you gotta figure how many people you're paying off, you know. It's a lot of money to make, but there's a lot of bills incurred. Gotta pay for the product out of the cash that comes in. And then you gotta pay the workers. So you got the payoffs and the workers, and then you have what's left. Sometimes all of it's left. Sometimes none of it's left. I've still got the same goal. Might take a little longer. See, a lot of it is on paper. Like, if I left the business, I could collect it. But it's out there. There's about fourteen grand owed me in the street. That should never be more than maybe six grand, but money is tight. I got to lean a little bit more, let 'em know I need mine, and it works."

He paused and sighed again. "One reason I haven't had time to see you is that I really been leggin it, you know, to get ahold of some cash. And besides, it's fuckin risky."

"Yeah," I said, "I know."

"Everybody tells me I'm crazy," he said, "cause there's nothin in it for me, not really."

"Well," I said, squirming internally, "I want you to trust me."

"Mmm," he said, looking at the floor. "Mmm. Mmm. Yeah. Well, let's think about it."

We went back into the living room, and with some relief I quickly admired his chess set from Mexico.

"You like to play chess?" I asked.

"Yeah. Like I don't know all the strategy and shit, but I know what each piece can do. I just figure I can do anything well. You got to be willing to do anything one hundred percent. If you're gonna be, well, whatever, be one hundred percent or leave it alone. And that's what I think makes people good at whatever they do. If you put your all in it. Like this apartment. When I took this apartment, this room was blue. Dig it, dark blue. They had linoleum on the floors, and it was dirty. Whoever had this apartment before didn't have too good a taste, at any rate. And I did it all. I put the shelves on the wall, put the lamps in the ceilings myself, put the dimmer switches in, wired the speakers in every room, painted, everything. And people come in now and look at the apartment and say, how'd you do it? Like, Jesus Christ, one hundred percent effort."

Jimmy rolled some more joints and turned up a tape of Dionne Warwick singing *Promises, Promises.* We sat down and leaned back and listened.

"Hey, have you noticed this?"

I hadn't realized I had closed my eyes until at that instant they popped open. Jimmy was standing by the large television, *TV Guide* in one hand, the other on the dial. "Dig this. Wait a minute. Wait'll you see. Dig it now, dig it!"

The color came on. He turned the dial a notch to another channel, and then another and another, all of them. "Can you dig that color? Every channel is perfect." He looked into the *TV Guide,* then switched back to the first channel. A movie was about to come on. He came over and sat down on the sofa and stretched his legs out and crossed them. He folded his arms and gestured at the television with his elbows. "Isn't that worth lookin at? List price on that set is eight hundred dollars. I bought it for three-fifty, hot. I'll get you one if you want. Or you know that smaller one in the kitchen? The portable? I can get that for you for, uh, let me think a minute. What did I pay for that? I think it lists for something like three-fifty. I paid about one-fifty. I can get you one for one-fifty. Just let me know."

Then, through a complementary coke-and-reefer warp, we watched the bells and robes and miracles and advancing and retreating suns and nuns in *The Miracle of Our Lady of Fatima.*

7

Jimmy was on the phone. "Hey, you remember that baby was up here last week? Yeah, well, her sister is around. . . . You been down to the movie? . . . Yeah, and also I got ahold of the rings on that matter. . . ."

He hung up and leaned over to pick up a joint. He lit it and turned to me. "See, that was all code. Baby—that's coke. That's what that means. And we talked about the movie, had he been down to the movie—that's about reefer. Then we talked about a ring, that's my new roscoe, my new gun. You never know about the phones."

He took a deep drag on his reefer, and held the lighted tip under his nose. "Yeah, yeah, it can be done. It can be done. That was one of my suppliers. He's becoming an ex-supplier. He is retiring. He wants to sell his apartment for about five thousand dollars, leave all his furniture and shit right in it and sell it and get out. I think he sold about fifteen keys every three or four weeks for about six months. He's *got* to have three or four hundred thousand dollars. Bought a home for his parents. Hey, when you get it that big, when you really get a nest egg, cut it loose. It's getting there that is the thing. But it can be done. You work your way up."

"Are you working your way up?" I asked.

"Shit yeah. Takes a little time, a little luck."

"How many guys in this area are dealing on your level?"

Jimmy pursed his lips. "Well, let's say in a ten-block radius, I'd say about three or four on *my* level. But now *dealers,* there might be three or four *hundred* that call themselves dealers, because everybody who sells drugs is a dealer of sorts. And *users,* wheew! But then you get into a thing like how do you tell who's a dealer and who's a user, you know. I'm on a high level now as far as I'm concerned. I've worked out a thing where I get half the stuff with cash, and half on consignment. We're talking about a seven-, eight-thousand-dollar package. Not that many people have that for coke. Guys above me are only above me in dollars and cents."

"What else is there," I asked, "besides dollars and cents?"

"Well, look at it this way: I provide a guy above me with an outlet. Hell no, he's not really on a higher level. Without me, what would he do with it? It's not that easy coming off with large quantities of drugs.

"But, okay, start at the beginning. Now here's a cat and he buys at a very low level, and deals on the lowest level, right to the street. So he's a pusher. He sells ten-dollar blows, twenty-dollar caps and shit. So he wants to get a little higher, and his dough is getting a little longer, so he buys bigger, right? But he's still going through a man that's coming to me. Now the pusher might know that it's me that the last man is coming to. But for the pusher to come directly to me, you know, you just don't do that. Who the fuck are you? There's people at that low level who know that I deal in good coke. But they couldn't fuckin mess up their faces and come to me and ask me for no drugs. I'll bust 'em in the head. Like nobody off the street comes up to me and says he wants to buy a bag. I don't *talk* to those motherfuckers. They don't come *near* me. That's the way it works, just like the Army. I don't talk to the cat that's two or three levels above me. I talk to my supplier. He talks to the organization above him.

"Now, a lot of times I'm not out there selling anything. I'm just out there making sure that the cats that are selling for me are selling. I'll be in the bar where I hang, and there'll be maybe two people in there selling stuff for me. And I have people who won't buy from them. Like one cat will come to me and he'll say"—Jimmy pouted his lips and jammed his chin onto his chest and affected a deep, raspy voice—" 'Hey Jim, I want to buy from *you*.' And I'll say, 'Hey, man, you know that's my product.' And he'll say, 'Yeah, but I'd still rather get it from you, man, cause I don't know that motherfucker. He could be messin with me.' Cat will talk like that cause, shit, he wants to be comin directly to me. It's a prestige thing for him. But I know the dude, so I go for it. But usually you don't do that shit. You deal with the man at the right level."

"What if a guy came across some big money suddenly," I asked, "and wanted to make a jump up?"

"No. See, if you were buying twenty dollars' worth of coke regularly, and suddenly you went to the cat who's been selling you twenty dollars' worth of coke and ask him for a thousand dollars' worth of coke—hey, that's not real. Cat who's buying small quantities of coke suddenly shows up with ten G's. Hmmm, where'd he get the money all of a sudden? Will he be coming back? Could be the PO-lice. Police do that shit. Suppose the CIA or the FBI or the Secret Service or whatever came to me and said, listen, we want you to become an undercover man for us. If you don't, we're gonna kill you, or whatever. For some reason like that I become undercover. You know how many people would go to the penitentiary? You know how many people I could bust? I could dry up New York damn near, by what I know. So all of a sudden I'm undercover. I don't act different. But people start gettin popped here and here and here, you know. Maybe I'll take a fall to make it look good, buy my way out of it. In the business, they call that going bad. And it's dangerous. Who isn't vulnerable? Man who busts you has the right to say I'm gonna put you in jail for thirty-five fuckin years, unless—Hey! Thirty-five years? Ooh, fucker gonna give up *God* for thirty-five years. Shit, for thirty-five *months,* man. Whew! So you watch out for cats with that big bread all of a sudden. Cats don't just jump upstairs like that, one day with nothin, the next day with big bread. You don't want to touch a cat like that. To know who the big man is is one thing, but to approach him is a no-no. You work up.

"Here's a man, say, that buys a thousand dollars' worth of coke every week, every week. And all of a sudden he starts buying two thousand—that's not too big a jump—but he's steady with it. Now, you figure that the extra thousand is maybe not his. He's buying it for somebody else. But by now you know the cat, you've watched him. And then after a while it goes to three thousand. But his thing is still consistent, so that means that someone else is in it, *stayin* in it. So now the cat comes to you and he says he's been spending good money and now he wants to meet the man you cop from and do a direct thing. In other words, let's say you do it consistently every two weeks and every two weeks, then you can demand a bigger man, maybe not the top cat, but somebody.

"That's like how it was with me. There's a cat that I used to buy through. He used to get my coke for me. And I started buying bigger and bigger, through the same cat. But it was consistent. And I got to the point where I was buying more coke than he was buying. He could get it, but I knew that my supply outlet was bigger than his. So I said, like tell your man that I want to meet him because, you know, otherwise I'll take my business elsewhere.

"What happens is that if you been doing it long enough and you sound reliable enough—cause people get checked out, you get to hear things and whatnot—you get to know the dudes involved. You feel your way, and eventually— well, in my case he finally said to bring me by, he'd like to

79

meet me. So he cut me into him directly. So now this dude that I used to buy from, for a while he and I were on the same level, buying from the same man. Now he's still where he was and occasionally when he can't get in touch with that man he comes to me for product, so actually I have moved above him.

"You see, the whole thing is getting yourself in a position to cop big. Now, I got three or four levels of guys between me and the street, for safety. Trying to get further away from it, the further the better. And the guy below me, he has to want to be a small *me*. He's aspiring to get to where I am, and I'm aspiring to get to the top. And as I move up it creates a void that he can fill, if he's got the ambition, if he really wants the cash, and unless he takes a fall. It's a constant struggle, you know, until you get there. The trouble is, you get to a level and something goes wrong and you go toooosh, and you got to start all over again. But once you get there—aaaaah!"

Jimmy arrived a little late for an appointment with a friend. The friend sat behind a desk, and I lounged in the corner. Jimmy walked wearily in and sagged into a chair. His applejack cap was tilted forward, and he stared down at his brown alligator shoes.

"This is a shit-black day, man," he said softly. "One of my men got washed out last night. Five slugs. He croaked, man."

"Is it in the papers?" the friend asked.

"Who reads the papers? Cat owed me about nine hundred dollars. I guess it's gone." Then he looked up and smiled lamely. "Maybe I can get it from the widow."

He had been delayed because he had stopped by to see the widow.

"How's she taking it?" I asked.

"She's okay."

80

"Okay?"

"Well, like she's cryin and sobbin and all that. But she's all right."

His voice trailed off, and he got up and walked over to look out the window, down on Lenox Avenue where the Cadillacs were gathering. "She's better off, I think, without that dude. Shit. It happens every day."

I asked him if he knew who did it, or if he cared.

"Naw. He's dead. Can't bring him back. Could have been a stickup. He wasn't with anybody, he was alone, which is a no-no. I think he was gonna rough off somebody that owed him some cash. On the other hand, it may not have been that way. Might have been over some broad. Could have just been some jealous dude. I don't know. Don't anybody know anything on the street when a killing's involved. Shit, would you? But he wasn't important. If they were trying to hit my operation they wouldn't go to him, they'd go to me. He was just an avenue. That avenue has closed up. Another avenue will open up. That's part of the day. The object is to make more than you lose. Some days you lose all of it. Some days you don't lose any. Right now it is tough out there."

8

Jimmy spun the cylinder on a new Baretta .32 automatic and held it between our faces, smiling slightly. He spoke softly. "Do you know how much a silencer is worth? Hmmm?"

"No."

"I can get a silencer for a thousand dollars. That's because it's me. Another cat might pay three, four thousand. I doubt if *you* could get one at all. Cause it's entirely illegal, you know, there's no legitimate reason for even *making* a silencer. I'm getting a silencer. For this gun."

He toyed with the gun in his hand, and then traced his finger around the end of the barrel. "See how the barrel extends just a little? It will take a silencer. It's got to be just the right size for the threads. I got one on the way. And I need it."

"Something wrong?" I asked.

"It's just hot out there, man. I don't know what it's because of, but man, they are bustin people left and right. You got to be super-careful, super-cool. I'm not even carrying nothin in the street these days. I take orders, set up a meeting. But it's so hot out there, man, I'm thinking about getting into another game."

He flicked his lighter and put it to a joint. Then he stalked across the room and turned on the radio to some rock. "Cats gettin flagged, man. Narcos becoming intensified. You saw the paper? They've got two hundred new narcos out there, and maybe they're being felt. They flagged my reefer man yesterday."

"Your *reefer* man?"

"Yeah. You know I started with reefer, right, years ago? Never cut loose what you begin with, because when shit gets up tight—I've gone back to reefer many times, cause it's the mildest of the busts, and everybody uses it. This month I sold, oh, about forty pounds of reefer. Now they busted my reefer man, flagged him yesterday. They been watchin him. They *had* to see me. They just didn't know who they were lookin at. Hey, I got friends of mine getting twelve years, fourteen years, twelve-to-fifteen. And if you don't think that's *serious*. Wheew! That's fire and brimstone, man."

Jimmy sneezed and rubbed his nose with the back of his hand. He paced and did a step with the music. Then he sneezed again and again. "Coke gives me the sneezies," he said, showing a wispy smile. "You know what? I think I'll get a job. I'm serious. That's how hot it is." He hummed with the music, and I tested the weight of the .32 in my hand, imagining the damped "tschew, tschew" of the firing sound through the silencer.

"Yeah, shit. B.J. got busted."

The gun went limp in my hand. "B.J.?" I said, stunned by his vulnerability.

"Yeah," Jimmy continued matter-of-factly. "Broke some dude's jaw or collarbone or something. Just a personal beef. But he was AWOL, so it's a real bust. Nothing I can do about that. He's in the brig now. I guess he was AWOL about two or three months, and just kept puttin off and puttin off goin back. But he only has a little time left to serve, so he'll put in for an early out. He'll be back."

He paced around the room, snapping his fingers and hitching in his elbows to the beat of the music. It was not altogether mercy which kept my thoughts on B.J., for I had been looking forward to getting to know him and his work better.

"How will you operate without B.J.?" I asked.

He shrugged. "The same way I did before I had B.J. I

don't have a lot of static, you know, way I do business. I'm pretty well set up, and nobody fucks me."

"Will you hire somebody else to do his work?"

"Naw. Most things you got to take care of yourself anyway."

"I thought you could just give a junkie a few bucks to do almost anything," I said, "even have somebody hit."

"What? Hey, I don't hire junkies to do *nothin*. Sure, there's hungry dudes all over the place, but you're lookin for somebody reliable, so don't deal with junkies. There's some crazy motherfuckers out there, wheew! Guys got nothin to lose. They don't know fear. They'll come right into your house after you. Shit, they're so dangerous they're dangerous to themselves. Like I hear right away when there's a thousand dollars out on a guy. Shit, there's motherfuckers around here kill God for a thousand dollars. Personally, I wouldn't let a junkie do nothin for me, uhn-uhn. They're not dependable. They're sick. So here's a sick junkie dude that I give a thousand dollars to and I say I want so-and-so killed. So he goes to so-and-so and says, 'Jimmy sent me to kill you for a thousand dollars.' And so-and-so says, 'Is that a fact? Well, here's fifteen hundred if you will kill *him*.' Or some shaky junkie walks in on you to kill you for me, and he starts shootin up and gets you in the leg. Then that means you are comin after me. Uhn-uhn. No bet. I don't put no money out to get nobody hit.

"Now, if you mean pay somebody to take some guy off, you mean kick his ass, that's different. That doesn't mean kill him. That's another matter. Maybe it's worth fifty dollars to some crazy dude to bust somebody's ass for you. If you get busted kickin a man's ass, that's just a bust for a street fight. If you get busted with a gun, that's attempted murder —and then a sick junkie starts mouthin about who sent him, that is gettin jammed, man, and I mean jammed."

"So you don't have *anybody* working for you?"

Jimmy chuckled and put off the answer while he opened his coke pouch and snorted a two-and-two. Then he sighed. "You were askin me if I got anybody to take B.J.'s place. I got about twenty people working for me now, different levels, different jobs. I have people that I just use sometimes. I got a thing going where there's a lot of people every day want to go to work for me. They say, 'Hey, man, let me do something for you, cause I got a boss thing.' But I don't need any more people working for me, half-ass slick dudes that are gonna jam my money up and make me hurt em. Every time you try to do something for a motherfucker that wants in, you end up getting jammed. Every now and then I'll take somebody new on, after I watch em for a while, check their shit out, you know. But not often."

Jimmy picked up two ashtrays and took them to the kitchen and dumped them. He brushed off the sofa, straightened the row of magazines, launching the usual ploys toward heading for the street.

"Like I got a dude that's really really beholden to me," he said as an afterthought. "Cause I really did him some solids, you know. And he's a butch kid. He's like B.J., only he doesn't use karate. He's just super-violent. Like say I got something comin up next week and I need somebody's ass kicked bad. I just say I want you to do me a favor, and it's done. Pay him nothin. He owes me, and I know he's dependable.

"See, he got in a little jam, took a fall for assault and shit. And when he got out he had a dispossess from his apartment, his wife and new baby about to be put out into the street. I gave him a couple hundred dollars. Then I have him do things. He won't even ask me for anything to get high, cause he's a proud cat."

He walked into the bedroom and I followed. He began pawing through his outfits on the rack, bringing out one and then another to lay them across the bed and ponder the

85

evening's selection. "Well, it's nice to be nice," he continued, "when you can. Because if it was reversed, and I was on my ass, I think he'd do it for me. And in this game what goes around comes around. You may be king of the hill today, a fall, and tomorrow you're on the bottom and somebody else is king of the hill. And if on the way up you've kicked everybody in the ass—hey, when you get down here, forget it."

He held up a pair of black boots and a pair of black alligator shoes for comparison. He shook his head. "I never used to have any trouble when I didn't *have* any clothes," he said with a sigh. For a minute he considered a black velvet outfit, then thought better of it.

"Yeah, I got to move out. I got a dude that I used to do business with. Cat owes me some money, and like, man, he's fucking me around. And I got a feeling that this is gonna cause a war, a sho-nuff sho-nuff war. I sent word that I wanted my cash, maybe twenty-six, twenty-seven hundred. I would not like to have to go to war with him, but I will."

His dark expression lightened. "But see, I can't press too hard because Slick owes him some money. That's this cat's holdout, cause the cat feels that if he pays me, Slick won't pay him. But Slick's gonna pay him, cause he got it in good faith. And you live by your reputation."

"I'll bet," I said, wincing at a shiny green shirt with some sort of gold scrollwork, "you have a good reputation."

"I think I got a boss reputation. People know that if I say, okay"—he clapped his hands once—"this is what you got comin to you, you gonna get it. I don't jam people up too tough. But you know, this is a business where people can push you around, and I don't get pushed too tough either."

Jimmy was getting fidgety now, frustrated by his indecisiveness about his clothes, watching the clock. He was moving a little more quickly between the bed and the closet.

"It's a rat race, man," he mumbled, "a rat race. You can have big money today and be broke tomorrow. Following day you have big money again. Comes that way. Like I'll leave here today, make my stops . . ." He stood still for a moment and grimaced and rubbed his stomach. "But you know what? I have found that it really really messes my system around. Really messes my stomach up. I don't drink alcohol. No cigarettes. But I get run down. Tired, man, worn out."

"Why don't you take a vacation?" I suggested.

"Vacation? Shiit. I took a vacation once, came back, and it cost me about nine hundred dollars in the business cause I wasn't here to oversee what was goin on. And that was just for a weekend."

"Well, you have to relax sometime," I said.

"H-e-y-y-y," he said, smiling and stretching his arms slowly away from his chest. "When I get it, man, when I *get* it."

9

As we were riding one day, police cruisers around, people looking at the car, it seemed to me only logical that Jimmy should be followed.

"Why *don't* you get followed?" I asked.

"Who by?"

"The police, of course."

"What for?"

"Well, for chrissake, because you're dealing drugs."

He raised his eyebrows and looked at me out of the corner of his eye. "You think that's obvious?"

"Well, not obvious, I guess," I said, "but here you are, driving an Eldorado. If a cop followed you for a couple days, he would have you, wouldn't he?"

Jimmy shrugged. "But *why* would he follow me, unless . . ." He chuckled. "Unless you *told* him."

"Mmm," I said, looking out the window.

"Look," he said, "okay, here's a young man, looks like he's under thirty, driving a Cadillac that's fly. But what is that saying? Look at all the Cadillacs around here. Don't you know young people driving Cadillacs who aren't hustlers? And man, the *number* of hustlers around here, whew! And not all of them deal in drugs. But let's say the Police Department assigned one man to follow each guy they thought was dealing drugs of *some sort*. There would not be any policemen left in the street.

"Now, in the bars, sure," he went on, "might be some

people figure what you do. Maybe there are some dudes be happy to run it to the police for a few dollars. But to figure is one thing, to know is another, to be nosy gets you killed. In the bars where I hang, everybody is known. Somebody walks in that isn't known, and tsssh, everything stops. You're the police, whoever the fuck you are, whatever color you are, until somebody that is known proves otherwise. I say *proves,* man. You walk in there with somebody not known and you better be ready to prove it, because there'll be some suspicious dudes ready to follow you out. That's real."

We watched police cruisers pass slowly by illegally parked cars, junkies nodding on doorsteps, an old woman known to carry heroin under her bandanna who stood in a doorway, and so on. "But if some cop just felt like stopping you," I said, "with what you got on you and in the car . . ."

"Hey," he said, "cops can't just stop you. They can't just do anything they want. Ten years ago maybe, or even five years ago they could. When I was a kid, if a cop said move, you moved. Look at these kids today, look at 'em in the street. They'll say, 'Kiss my ass, man, I'm not movin nowhere!' Why? Not more rebellion. Just because cops have been playing it God-like for so long. And people are hip to the fact that they're not God. People won't go to jail like they used to. They don't accept what used to be automatic. You watch when a cop stops somebody nowadays in Harlem. A crowd gathers right away to see what's coming off. That's why as soon as the police get a beef the first thing they do is get you in the car and get you away from there. I think they tell the cops at the stationhouse, above all watch out for the riot. Don't cause no riot. So the cops are smart about that. They are professional—shit yeah, cops in this town are probably the best there are, from the standpoint of knowing how to handle a situation."

We rode in silence for a while. "I don't know," I said. "If

I carried the stuff you do, did what you did, I don't know what I'd tell a cop."

"Oh, *man*," Jimmy said with a pained expression. "Cops got no right to . . . Hey, listen. The police stopped me the other night, Friday night, up here in Harlem. My taillights weren't working. So the cop stopped me and told me my lights were out. I jiggled the switch, and they went off and on, cause the electrical system had a short. So at that point the cop could see that something was wrong with the switch. And it makes sense that I wouldn't know that, because, you know, it's a new Eldorado. Okay, so this cop was very polite, and I was very polite—that is always my come-on, I am not belligerent—and I showed him my license and registration, and he was satisfied.

"Now, at this point his partner got out of the car. Dig that it was two white cops in Harlem. The first cop was satisfied, now his partner wants to hassle me. 'Where you goin?' this second cop says. Where am I goin? Where am I *goin?* What do you mean, where am I goin? None of your fuckin business where I am goin."

"You talk like that to a cop?" I said. "Isn't that asking for trouble?"

"What? Let me explain something: There are things the police can do and can't do, unless you let them. Hey, if you cower to the motherfuckers and quiver, first thing they'll do is say, 'Open the trunk of your car!' That's illegal, but they do it every day. They do it so regularly that they don't expect any static. Here's a young black dude in a Cadillac, we'll just fuck him around. But when you come off with, 'None of your fuckin business,' they know they can't do that shit."

"Supposing you annoy them and they arrest you," I said, "even on some silly charge."

"Bet that! Arrest me! Take me to the station, and what do they tell the sergeant at the desk? My taillights were out? Now, the sergeant doesn't know who I am. Think about it.

There's some hustlers out there that know some righteous motherfuckers, so they got to be careful. The sergeant doesn't want to get in any trouble just because this one cop is sore. And I am polite to the sergeant."

"What if they're all trying to shake you down?"

"That's not real, because then the first cop would have started it. But, okay, you get to the stationhouse, and it comes off like a shakedown. Then you rap: 'Listen, I know this is a shakedown. You know this is a shakedown. And when my lawyer gets here, I'm gonna sue you motherfuckers, cause I got the time *and* the money.' See, that's the whole gimmick. You gotta be willing to take it to the max."

"Supposing they just wanted to rough you up, or they frisked you and found your gun and some drugs?"

"Hey, frisk *me?* How? They can't frisk you, not because your taillights were out. They must have reason to think that you are a felon. And listen: I'm not gonna stand and let anybody feel me, touch me. I don't allow that shit. In order to take me to the stationhouse they either got to be arresting me, or taking me for questioning. Taking me for questioning, they cannot touch me. And they got no felony charge to arrest me on. What the fuck are you just gonna be pattin on me for?

"And rough me up? It would not be cool of them even to try, because nine out of ten of them I think I could kick their ass. Shit, I'm a brown belt in karate. Two uniformed cops? And if it comes to a takeoff thing in the street, don't forget this is Harlem. Now, they pull their guns, they better mean to shoot, because I'll try and kill both of them, and I have the edge because I know what I'm about to do, and they don't.

"But see, again you have to dig, if you're a cop you deal with people. If a cop walks up on a cat, and he comes down a certain trail, out of a certain bag, you know what he's gonna accept and not accept. A cop gets to know these things just like I do. Oh sure, there's some cops who have to

91

prove themselves every day, their manhood is in doubt. Some cops will fuck you around, plant stuff on you to make a bust and shit. Oh yeah. That's why they get killed every day. You remember that time those two cops—somebody put in a call that something was wrong, and the two policemen showed and got out of the car, and a sniper was waiting for their ass? You wanna know why? Cause those two motherfuckers had kicked somebody in the ass, had fucked somebody around. And that same somebody was waiting on their ass when they showed. That's why you read about cops gettin blown away. For no apparent reason some fuckin dude shoots a cop. But there's a reason.

"So I always come on nice, but don't think that means I'm stupid or that I'm gonna let you ultra fuck me around. I'll take it wherever it's necessary. These two dudes that stopped me, they're not detectives, you know. Detective stops me, I'd be very cool, careful. Because a detective can watch you and fuck with you. A uniformed cop can't do that.

"So anyway, this motherfucker says, 'Where ya goin?' And I said, 'Listen man, if you're not fuckin satisfied, arrest me.' And as I said that, I opened my car door and got in and slammed it and started my car and split."

The next night I finally reached Jimmy by phone at ten o'clock. "Yeah, we can rap for a little while," he said. "Be here by ten-thirty, because I have to leave by eleven."

I was calling from midtown Manhattan, a good half-hour away. I sped uptown, intending to turn onto the West Side Highway. But as I turned left, I saw that the entrance was barricaded for some reason. So I continued turning in a "U" and zoomed back toward the avenue. As I came to a red light, a helmeted policeman on a motor scooter putted up and waved for me to stay. I checked my watch and rolled down the window.

"What's the trouble?" I said.

"Illegal U-turn," he said, his summons pad already out.

"Bullshit," I said.

"License and registration," he said.

I threw open the door and sprang out, at the same time slapping my license and registration, which were in order, across his summons pad. I then produced a loud stream of expletives, challenges, and threats, culminating with the notice that he was a helmeted head shorter than I, the meaning of which was clear if he wanted to start something. Several passersby seemed startled, and the policeman looked up at me with wide eyes. He said nothing. He wrote out the summons with unheard-of speed, and as I snatched it from him and jumped into my car and split, I could see that he was straddling his scooter and staring after me, his pad still in his hand.

Phyl opened the door, and I stalked past her and barged into the living room, still charged with obscenity. Phyl followed me in. Jimmy was seated on the sofa, a supper tray on his lap. Slick and his woman were seated too, and all were staring at me. I slammed down my gloves on the table and bellowed out my tale.

"Hold it, hold it, hold it," Jimmy said softly, his fork poised in the air. In that instant my eye caught two pistols, three joints of marijuana, and a hillock of cocaine in a blurred panorama. "Take it easy," Jimmy continued, his voice soothing.

"Yeah," Slick said, also calm. "We'll get you a license by tomorrow, if that's the hangup—New York, New Jersey, whatever. Take it easy."

There was a moment of nearly silent heavy breathing.

"Whew!" Jimmy said. "You said *what* to the cop? Hey! Well, it could have been worse." He took a bite of something.

"How?" I asked.

"Could have been *me*," he said. "When you push like that, man, you got to be ready to take it to the max."

I was suddenly awake to the perils of identification with my subject. His preaching was not, after all, meant for *me* to practice. I accepted with trembling fingers the joint offered me by Slick.

The art of bribery, akin in certain ways to negotiating the price for a used car, is an integral part of the hustler's repertoire. "It's where your cool comes in," Jimmy told me. "You got to have a sense of the situations."

Like speeding. "Couple cops stopped me the other day on the Triborough Bridge, said I was doin sixty in a fifty-mile-per-hour zone. I had the Cruise Control set at fifty, but it's not worth a hassle. But the cops let you know where it's at, indirectly. Like it was the end of their shift and whatnot. They didn't want to give me no ticket. They wanted money. So it comes off like, I say, 'Hey listen, I need my license, cause I make my living by driving. What could we do about this?' Now, a cop will never say, 'Give me fifteen dollars.' So he says, 'You're doin the talkin.' Okay, now what they usually expect is that you will fold up some money, ten, fifteen dollars, inside your license and hand it to them. Not me."

Jimmy grabbed my forearm and twisted my palm up and slapped his palm down on mine.

"Just like that. I just paid you. I put the open money right there in the cop's hand. They don't like that at all. They jumped in their car and cut out, leavin rubber—screeee! They didn't know who I was. I could of been from the D.A.'s office. I like to fuck with 'em like that. But of course I didn't put no money in his hand until he lets me know that it's cool. You learn that."

Then there are the street games, like dice. Jimmy likes the dice games because it is a good place to make contacts, a good place to watch where the cash is flowing.

"Uptown the other night we had a big dice game goin on," he said. "First the uniformed cops came by in the car, and the players gave them five dollars apiece, ten dollars. Then an hour or so later another car comes by with a black cop and a white cop and a sergeant. So they gave them twenty dollars—five dollars for each of the cops and ten dollars for the sergeant. Don't you know that twenty minutes later here comes two motherfuckin detectives, two narco detectives. They gave them some money, I don't know just how much. Now at this point, had any more cops come, it would have been a bitch out there, cause they had pushed it to the bust. They had really pushed it to the wire. Somebody would have said fuck them cops, and they would have kept on playing. And then the cops would have got out the car because they didn't get no money, and they're maybe dumb enough to start hassling people. And that's how shit starts. You hear how a cop gets stabbed, fight breaks out, ten people get arrested. Because people get tired of being hassled, man. God damn! How many people do you have to pay off to have a dice game out in the street?

"Look, I can understand a uniformed cop looking for two dollars, five dollars out in the street. He's out there hustlin. He wants to get some money to take home to his wife and kids, or whatever. Okay, they're money-hungry because they're human. But do you know how much they make a week in bribes? Do you know that if there's five crap games, and they come around every two hours and get ten dollars, five dollars apiece, all night long, and if they do that five days a week, do you know how much they're gettin in graft? And that's the lowest form. They got regular joints, after-hours spots, that give em fifteen, twenty dollars a night. They give that to the cop on the beat. Now, you got four or five of these spots giving you fifteen, twenty dollars a night, and you got the dice games—how much you making on graft? Your pay ain't shit compared to what you can make on graft. People don't respect the police anymore like they used to because, fuck 'em, they're men, just like you and I. And they're hustlin illegal shit."

"Maybe dice games aren't so important," I said, "compared to bigger payoffs, like for drugs."

"Hey, listen, how can you tell me you're a good cop if you'll take a ten-dollar bribe to let a dice game go on? If you'll take a dollar, you'll take a million. If a cop will take a bribe, he'll take a bribe, he'll take a bribe. If he can get away with it. Offer him enough and you'll get away with murder."

"Isn't that stretching it a bit?"

"Damn no. What happens if you take five dollars off the dice game instead of breaking it up, and you leave, and a fight breaks out and some poor slob gets stabbed to death over that dice game—which *happens*. It is the cop's fault because his job says that he should have broken up the dice game. That's what he gets paid to do. If he's going to be a one-hundred-percent good-guy cop for real, he don't take no bribes. But I don't know any like that. Do you? So if you're a cop, don't fuck around and tell me that I'm a hustler and fuck me around, cause I'm not goin for it. Cause I know where *you're* at."

Jimmy looked at his watch as he paced back and forth. "I'll have to cut this short," he said. "I got to go to traffic court. Shit. Running a red light. I wasn't givin no cop no bribe, because I was in the right—the light was just changing as I went through."

"Just your word against the cop's?"

"Yeah, well, I'll give it a try, cause I'm in the right. Also I got two other violations on my record, speeding and shit. I got a warning I was going to lose my license if I got any more points."

"That's not real," Jimmy said. "It just wouldn't come off that way."

We were looking at a clipping from *The New York Times*. The story said that two "undercover Federal narcotics agents" had shot and killed one and wounded another suspected cocaine dealer. The plot was that the two who were shot were to have delivered a kilo of cocaine to the two agents, and the agents were to pay $13,000. They reported, after the shooting, that the two suspected dealers were planning a double-cross, to hold the agents up for the money while not delivering the cocaine. The agents said that they were forced to shoot in self-defense.

"That's not real," Jimmy said again. "Nobody who deals that big is going to hold you up. It just wouldn't happen that way. Anybody who can handle a key of pure coke is dealing big, and they want to keep dealing, not just take off two dudes for a little cash. Either the cops were just gunning them for some reason, or the two cats found out the guys were agents and came ready for a shoot-out. Wouldn't surprise me if the two cats never did have cocaine to deal, and were just puttin somethin over on the cops. But the way this reads, it's not real. I'd love to know what really happened."

There are more than twenty-five million hand guns in the United States, of which Jimmy has about six (the number changes as new ones are bought, old ones discarded—but he always buys new, never a used gun that might be traceable to an old crime). Although as a drug dealer he is a man in constant danger from the law, Jimmy does not carry the guns primarily for protection against the police. "The *last* thing I want to do," he told me once, "is shoot a cop in New York City. They get you for that. You *never* hear of anybody gettin away with shootin a cop."

So, along with the guns, Jimmy always carries a good hunk of cash in his pocket, some for style, some for "emergencies." When I first met him he might carry a thousand or so. On a more recent occasion he pulled from his pocket two bundles of bills held together by rubber bands. In one bundle I counted $500, in the other $5,000.

"The five hundred represents cash on hand," he said, "like I bought a suit the other day that's very bad—it goes that way. The five G's, that's emergency money, for the police. Like you hope to get off with a grand or whatever, but with the weights I'm dealing now, it might take five G's."

Jimmy has never yet been busted for carrying or selling drugs himself, but he has been involved in payoffs and losses along a broad scale.

"One night this cat gave me a call at the bar where he was, said he got flagged. He was calling from a pay phone at this corner in Brooklyn where they busted him. They busted him with just some reefer and a little coke, but his car was dirty, so he didn't want the bust. Cause if they arrested him they would take him to the station and search his car. And the cops didn't want the bust, they wanted money. That's why they let him make the call.

"When I showed, I showed clean, I mean clean clear through—no gun, no nothin, cause, hey, they could have just been waitin for another guy to come so they could arrest him too. So I'm clean. I park my car around the corner and walk. I see my man and I say, 'Hey, man, what's happenin? Haven't seen you in a long time.'

"I'm just rappin to the dude and the two cops are just standin nearby not saying anything. The dude says, 'Hey, listen, man, I got into a little jam here. These two officers, you know, are arresting me.' I say, 'What? What happened? What did he do, officer?'

"You know, it's a game, a game. 'Uh, illegal possession of drugs.' I say, 'Oh wow. Hey listen, officer, he's a nice dude. He's got a wife and kids. What can be done? You don't want to flag him, you know, give him a break.'

"Now it's their move. See how they come on. Now the mere fact that they're there waitin means they don't want to arrest him. But still, see how they come on. 'Well, it's gettin late,' one cop says, 'and we're going off. We really don't want to make an arrest, and he seems like a nice guy . . .' You know, there's always a certain amount of bullshit in it. This is the game. It's never, 'What will it cost?' Cause they won't tell you. 'What's it worth?' they will say. Now, in this case it cost me three hundred dollars—one-fifty apiece."

"Your man didn't have anything on him?" I asked.

"Well, I think he had something like seventy dollars."

"Why didn't they just take that, rather than wait around and get another guy involved and all, take the risk of getting caught?"

"Because they didn't know how much they were going to get. Maybe I wouldn't be cool, maybe I would panic and give them a bundle."

"But how do you arrive at a price?" I asked. "Suppose that when you made your offer they said to double it?"

"Then I can't do it. I don't have it. I say, 'Well, just put the motherfucker in jail then, man, fuck you all.' Now one-fifty apiece is better than nothing. Cause if this mother-fucker goes to jail he goes to jail. It was his bust from the git-go. I'm going to try to prevent this, but I'm only trying s-o-o hard. So in this case I said, 'Hey, I got three hundred dollars. You want it?' "

"But how do you know how much it's worth, where to start?" I asked.

"It's only worth something reasonable. It's not worth something ridiculous. It's according to the bust. In this case, they only had him for a misdemeanor bust. You know what's reasonable and they know what's reasonable, and you know they want *something,* not the bust. So five hundred apiece is not reasonable for a little marijuana bust. Might be reasonable for a coke bust, cordin to what you're busted with. Now here's a man they bust with ten thousand dollars worth of coke. And he says I'll give you one hundred dollars apiece. No bet. Cop busts me with a five-dollar bag of reefer, that's a misdemeanor. I can see giving him one-fifty. Three hundred would be outrageous. But now, if they bust me with ten thousand dollars' worth of coke, shit yeah, I could see givin them five hundred apiece, or more. It's worth it."

"Isn't it worth *anything* to stay out of prison?"

"Listen, cop catches me with two ten-dollar caps of coke. I'm not giving him a thousand dollars if I can help it. I'm not going to prison either. I'm going to get a good lawyer, and the right judge will probably give me probation, suspended sentence—and the cop gets nothing. You dig what I'm saying? If the police want some money, you have to be willing to take the bust if it would not be worth the money they want. So both sides have to be reasonable.

"Now sometimes," he went on, "they take the bribe *and* your stuff. Those are the real nasty motherfuckers. My man came up here settlin some business. I gave him seventeen hundred dollars. Plus he had two pieces of coke worth six hundred each. And he had about nine hundred of his own cash. Okay, he goes downstairs. Here comes three local cops, two white and one black, writing out tickets for double-parked cars. His man is sittin down there in the car snortin—dumb dude snortin right in the car. They walk up on him and bust him for snortin. My man shows downstairs. 'That your car?' the cops ask him. 'Yes, that's my car.'

"Now they bring him into the hallway and start telling him how he's goin to jail. But my man says, 'Hey, you didn't bust me, you busted *him*. Now you can take him to jail if you want, but I'd like to have this thing squashed.' Now the white cops were going for it. But the black cop is hip—you can't bullshit black cops so easy. They know the ropes. They make me more nervous than white cops. This cop figures my man is into something, so he says, 'Okay, we'll impound your car, cause the man was in your car.'

"Oh shit, they got him. Cat's got a brand-new Buick Electra and it's dirty, can't stand a search. The end was they let the cops take 'em into the hallway—which is illegal and which you should never allow—instead of stayin out in the street. In the street the cop can't do nothin but either arrest you or take somethin quick. Can't have no ruckus in the street. In the street my man could have given them a quick hundred dollars. But in the hallway the black cop threw him up on the wall, got into his pockets, took it all out— all the coke, all the cash, even the three hundred dollars the man they caught snortin had in his pocket. Why did they take the cocaine? To sell it, of course. Cats were dishonest."

"There isn't much anybody could do about it in any case," I said, "once they've got you."

Jimmy narrowed his eyes. "Cats lost their cool. Don't go in no hallway. Don't allow no search. Be cool all the way through. Got to be icy. Like when Slick was busted. In that case, the faggot cop that busted him was paid off anyway.

"Why? It's like this: The cop makes a real bust, cause that's his job, and then he finds out you're into something and you've got some cash available. Now, you can't call the bust back. But the policeman has got to go and testify. According to how he testifies is according to what happens to you. A cop is a professional witness. So when he raps on you on the stand, he knows what to say that will jam you and not jam you. When he saw you throw a package to the ground, he can say he was fifteen feet away and the lighting conditions were excellent and word it so he jams you, or he can say he was thirty-five feet away and it was dark and word it so that a good lawyer can juggle it around and get dismissed. In Slick's case it was dismissed."

The New York Times reported the arrest of a man who had two kilograms of heroin which police valued at

$200,000. Detectives said they were offered a bribe of $3,000, then $6,000, which they refused. Finally when the figure went to $10,000, they "accepted" the money and made the bust.

"Well, you never know," Jimmy said. "Sometimes the money is the only chance you got, so you try it. This ain't no party game."

10

"You asked me what I would most like to do today, regardless of money, what I most wanted to do in the world. Well, I would say play football. No doubt about it. I would play football for nothin."

It was early one Sunday afternoon in the fall. The Jets were on TV, and Joe Namath, who was to break his wrist later in the season, was out there on his rickety knees directing the Jets.

"Shit yeah, that's what I'd do. Look at that Namath, knees and all. He is a tough motherfucker. All that pain. Yeah, but I'd do it too, if I could. My fuckin ankle."

The Jets were a yard from a touchdown. "Bet Namath will put his head down and drive those poor ol knees and take it in himself." Namath did just as Jimmy had predicted. As Namath jogged off the field, Jimmy bounced up off the sofa. "See that! See that! Namath is the *king!*" He seemed to be one of the crowd, clapping and cheering.

Jimmy was playing defensive back for a semipro team when he was spotted by a pro scout and invited to a tryout with the big team. "They sent me that contract I showed you," he said. "You know, fifteen-thousand-dollars minimum guarantee if you make the team. And they give you expenses and a per-diem type thing meanwhile. Doesn't amount to anything. Doesn't cost them anything to let a free agent try out. But I'd have made it. I watched those cats in my position. Hey, shit. Ha! I'd of eaten them up alive. I outweighed the guy by fifteen pounds, and I *know* I'm faster. So I filled out the contract and sent it back. Then seven weeks before training camp this fuckin car hits me and ruins my ankle." He pulled up his robe and rubbed the six-inch scar running down the lower part of his leg. "I was gonna kick his ass, but I was in too much pain."

Six months later he tried to ride a bicycle, and the pain made him give up after half a block. So football was over. But so was working nine-to-five. "I had always hustled a little, you know, as a kid even, part time. So I figured, fuck it. If I can't play football, I'm gonna make me some bread at least. And so that's when I became a full-time hustler."

As the Jets played on, Jimmy stared at the set and continued talking.

"I was born and raised in New York. I was a jitterbug, you know, a gang fighter. You just go around black neighborhoods and ask about the Chaplains, the Enchanters, the Mighty Dutchmen, the Seven Crowns, the Sportsmen. All these were clubs of boys in various neighborhoods. We wore club jackets and shit. We were very bad. We had a notorious reputation. We'd go anywhere, kick ass. Course we wouldn't stay in our own neighborhood, cause if *your* gang stayed in *your* part of town, and our gang stayed in *our* part of town, where would the fight come off? And we moved. Always for a reason, though, like when one of our guys would be out somewhere with his girl at a party and they'd rough him up, cause he was from our gang. That would start it.

"I wasn't president of the gang. I was war counselor. At the age of twelve I was carrying a gun, and I would shoot you quicker than I would shoot you today. When I was twelve my mother was killed by a junkie."

He related the ugly details of this weird tragedy, and of other more common familial disasters. Then he sighed.

"I became a hustler very easily, because I got it naturally. My pops was a hustler. But he was an educated hustler,

104

worked his way through college being a hustler. He was an ass-kicker, my mother said. When she met him, he was a con man. He had been a pimp, he had been everything, you know, and she was a sweet little college girl. And he took her off.

"Now, thinking about it, I think I was a bastard, you know, a product of the moment, when she was uptight, which I could halfway dig. Doesn't bother me anyway. My best friends are bastards. I pieced it together, things she told me, things my grandparents say. Things that when I met my father I heard him say.

"I met him once, not until after my mother died. I think I was thirteen. He was married to a white woman, owned a couple businesses, very, very wealthy. And I couldn't stand him. Not just his personality—cause I didn't know him that well—but the fact that he was so successful. He had everything that would make me want to look up to him, but I knew he wasn't correct. He was into some goodies, all right, super bourgeois. But that wasn't my shot. It's strange because, like I said, my father was good at what he did, and I guess I always envied that. I think one of the main reasons I wanted to play football was because he did—some prototype team that I don't think even exists anymore.

"But I disliked him just naturally, because of what I had heard about him. And then my mother's dead, and here he is. He shows with a white woman who was telling me, 'Call me mother.' She was very nice, you know, but it really upset me. I was going through a white-black thing as a kid, like gang fights because of the racial thing.

"There was a club called the Romans that we used to fight constantly. You see, we were all kids, between the ages of say eleven and fifteen. But these Italian kids, the Romans, well, their uncles and fathers and shit would be in it. Older men like needin shaves and shit. Maybe it wasn't their uncles and fathers. Seemed like it at the time. Maybe it

105

was their big brothers, like nineteen-, twenty-year-old cats we found ourselves fighting—grown men. And we were just kids. Shit, they were trying to hurt us.

"We lived in the projects, up in the Bronx. It was an all-white, all-Italian neighborhood, and they built a low-income project right in the middle of it. I was the first black kid in my grammar school, and there was trouble from the first. The principal told my mother, 'Well, some of these children here have never seen blacks before'—he'd have this sweet voice—'and that's why they tend to act a little hostile, but I'm sure that in time it will pass over.'

"And in the mean fuckin time I'm gettin my head kicked in every day. I was the first black kid, and Gabriel Smith was the second. We had to fight our way into school, out at lunchtime, back in after lunch, and on the way home at three. Every day we would get our asses like really reamed, to the point of getting teeth knocked out, really hurt. And there was nothing ever done about it. When we got to school the teacher would say to wash up. 'You look a mess, I told you about fighting and such.' But that was always the end of it.

"So one day on the way to school I told Gabriel I'm not gonna get my ass kicked no more. We were comin through the lot and we picked up some pipes. About a block from school they were waiting for us. By now it was sport for them, you know. So we took those pipes and like we did a job out there that day. It had always been with fists before, but always six or seven or eight to two. So we really fucked them up. Doctors had to be called. We really did a job with them pipes. Hey, there was a lot of vengeance in that shit.

"And so the police came to the school. And all these white kids with their parents. They bring us out of the classroom. Hey! *Our* parents aren't there. And the cops pushing us into the wall: 'Yeah, yer goin to jail for a long time.' I mean, you know, like I'm standin there listening to this shit, and I know that they're taking advantage of me. My mother's not even there! Everybody else's father and mother is there. But where's *my* mother?

"And then the detective came, white detective, and he rapped, more or less in our behalf, saying, 'You're telling me that these two boys attacked these seven boys?' I'll never forget his words. And all these outraged white parents suddenly realize that we were defending ourselves. And then the fact came out that we had been coming to school for weeks with black eyes and lumps and bumps and bruises and torn shirts and shit. And the principal said: 'All right, you all go on back to your classes.'

"That did something to me, you know, it really did. And since that time, I've never taken 'no,' I've never bit my tongue. And I'll get super-violent before the next guy can get to that point. I won't wait for you to hit me, I'll hit you. I was just the opposite before all this at school. I didn't like to fight. I was a nonviolent kid.

"Now, let's see. What happened next? My mother died. I went to reform school, a home for boys. My mother was dead and I was incorrigible. I'd been in the gang for a long time. I'd been expelled from school for fighting a lot of times. My sister had gotten married. She was older. She was then seventeen. I was thirteen. Her husband and her had separated. He was a very big dude, about twenty. And he roughed her off a few times, you know. And one day he grabbed her out by the park and I tried to kill him with a knife. Then I went upstairs and got my pistol and came back down. They caught me. I was gonna kill him. If I'd have gotten back to where he was, he'd have been killed.

"Yeah, I had a gun. You know how we used to get guns? Take the cops off. I didn't know any easier way as a kid. Where does a thirteen-year-old get a gun? Nobody was selling guns then. Like, we didn't know anybody selling guns. There was a young-looking cop. He was little, like

107

there were guys in the gang as big as he was. And we took him off, grabbed him, and kicked his ass. One of the fellows knocked him unconscious with a brick. We took his gun, his bullets, his handcuffs—everything but his badge. We were scared to take his badge.

"And it went off too easy. After we dug how easy it was, we took off a lot, you know, became rough. Then one time we really had to put a job on a cop in the subway. He was mad, he wasn't going for it, and he didn't go down like that young cop. Like at one point I began to doubt that we were going to get him, because it was a real scuffle. We took him off, but that was the last one we ever took off. We took about four or five cops off, took their guns, over a period of time."

The Jets' game was over. Neither of us knew how it had ended. Jimmy stretched, yawned, sighed, and said, "Excuse me just a minute." He went out and brought back his aluminum-foil packet of coke and the canister of grass. He snorted a two-and-two, rolled some joints, turned the radio on at low volume, leaned back in the sofa, and sighed.

"Let's see. After I stabbed my brother-in-law I went to reform school. I'd been busted lots of times before, gang fights and all. It had got to a point in grammar school where the racial prejudice was so vicious that I'd do anything if you fucked with me. And in junior high school, when we were fourteen, they had a police car that used to drive behind Gabriel and me and follow us home so that there wouldn't nobody fuck with us. But they weren't protecting us, they were protecting the white kids. Cause they would fuck around and start something, and we would finish it, because we had by this time become quite vicious. I guess if you fight every day, every day, every day, you get good at it. And we didn't lose often. Aaah, yeah. I haven't seen Gabriel since I went to reform school. Last time I heard he had become a very large dealer in Brooklyn."

108

Jimmy took the last deep drags on his reefer, and sneezed. Anne Murray was singing "Snowbird" over the radio. He hummed with it. I asked him how it affected him when his mother died.

"I don't know. Yes I do know. I'd just rather not talk about it. It jammed me up. I'm still jammed because of that.

"So then I ran away from reform school the first time, and my grandparents made me go back. I ran away again and got caught by the state police. Oooh, they put an ass-kickin on me that lasted a long time. I ran away a third time and got all the way back to New York. Myself and about four other boys just followed a railroad track, walked about three, four days, almost froze to death. That's the hungriest I've ever been in my life.

"I stayed in New York about two years, until I was sixteen. I had a room, job in a car-wash. I was on my own. What happened is, I got caught. I was at a party, and a kid got knifed. And the police showed and arrested everybody. And they found out that I was the kid they had been lookin for for two years. So they sent me back to reform school. But about a week later the judge let me go because I had done so good for those two years being on my own.

"Then I went to school for a while, a school for delinquent boys. I went there and graduated from junior high school and went into high school. Then I quit high school and went into the Air Force. Sure, I had no record. I had been a minor all this time.

"I could have liked the Air Force, but the same thing happened, same problem, everything was racial. I was in the military police. They are supposed to give you a bunch of tests when you go in the service, and you tell them what you want to be. I wanted to be a jet mechanic."

Jimmy chuckled. "Yeah, that's what I told them. But if you notice, there's not many black jet mechanics. There's a lot of white jet mechanics and a lot of black military policemen. Shit, it's not a bad job, but what do you learn? To be a policeman? Shiiit. Now, if you're a jet mechanic when you come out—you know what they pay at Kennedy International for jet mechanics? Shiiit." He chuckled again deeply.

"So I was in the military police. I also got married when I was eighteen. So I had a wife and a son—she had a son when I met her. She was seventeen. And for the next three years I took care of her seven brothers and sisters. Why? I think, well, they were all youngsters. Looking back on it, I think I needed the responsibility. And she was a beautiful girl. She was hungry. I thought I loved her, wanted to help her, so I married her. They all looked to me. When I didn't bring no food home, nobody ate.

"How it got started for me in the military police was I caught a cat goin over the fence. He drove a food truck. Now, I could have turned him in and got him thirty days in the stockade. I let him go. The following weekend he picked up his supplies and came by my house and dropped off a quarter of a truck of stuff, like three, four cases of canned milk, one of them whole things of cheese, couple cases of eggs—eggs went bad, we had so many.

"The cat was glad to do it. He would never rap on me. I could have killed him, cause I caught him on the fence. I knew it and he knew it. So I got that little thing going. I used to let him off the base when he wasn't supposed to be off the base, and every week he stopped at my house and unloaded. Then I began to hustle. There were all kinds of little hustles. . . ."

The phone rang and he let it ring twice before picking it up. "Yeah? Yeah. Hold on." He covered the mouthpiece with his hand and asked me urgently, "What's forty times sixteen?"

"Six-forty," I replied quickly.

He put his mouth back to the phone. "You know how

much that is a pound? There's sixteen ounces in a pound, so it comes to six-forty."

I was figuring again, and suddenly I thought I was wrong. "Eight-forty," I whispered. "Eight-forty, not six-forty, eight-forty!"

Jimmy nodded and continued. "Yeah, well I'm saying I don't think the man will take it because I think he can do better than that. It's even more than I said. It comes to roughly eight hundred and some dollars."

By now I was figuring on a yellow pad, trying to get my drifting synapses under control. The figure of six-forty appeared persistently, and at last I flashed the pad at Jimmy like a cue card. He saw it and closed his eyes.

"Wait a minute, hold on. Listen, I was wrong. It becomes six-forty a pound. Well, add it up yourself. Sixteen ounces in a pound. I don't think the man is gonna pay those prices. But I'll relay it and let you know tonight." He hung up.

"That was cut," he said to me. "Quinine. Dude wants $640 a pound. For *cut*. Hey, I've gotten it—well I've known people that have gotten it for two hundred a pound. Expensive, cause it's so h-a-r-d to get. But like *I* can do better than that. Shit, that fucker's insane."

He took the dwindling joint out of his mouth and held it at the very end, between the nails of his thumb and forefinger, to relight it.

"I got an early out," he said.

"An early out?"

"Yeah, from the Air Force. They busted me for being late, and took my stripes. It was harassment. A white officer decided to fuck me around, you know. But when he did, because of the amount of dependents I had, I just put in for an early out, and they let me out."

Jimmy sighed. "Yeah, shit, then I brought my wife here to New York. That bitch. She got slick. She was here two days and started talking shit out the side of her mouth. She

111

was a beautiful girl, and all the hustlers started fillin her head with shit right away, telling her about all the mink they'd buy her, and she went for it and got slick. I looked up one day and she was slicker than me. She wasn't a hooker. She was just givin it away. Broke my heart. I loved her. Well, I didn't love her. I thought I did.

"Anyway, that was the end of that. I haven't seen her for eight years or so. When I see her, I've got something for her. I don't know where she is. Bitch put me in jail for non-support. I was sick. They asked me to come to court. When I got to court I had a letter from the hospital—I had been in the hospital for about three weeks—and I had a letter from my job. I was starting back to work in a couple days. I owed $160 in back payments to her. And I went before a woman judge, and that bitch gave me thirty days, or $160 plus $100 security. Fortunately at this time there was this little broad who liked me very much and she had a little bit of cash in the bank. But I still stayed locked up six days before she could get me out. All the red tape and shit. I never paid my wife a penny after that. That bitch could be dead as far as I'm concerned. I know she's not dead. I've heard since then that she's had a couple more babies. I know she don't want to see me, cause I never did her any dirt, and she did it to me. So I owe her."

Jimmy yawned and sneezed. "We had a little girl. She died when she was three."

As he recounted that death from a childhood disease, I suddenly recalled another detail of his bedroom, a picture of a smiling little girl, with a garland of plastic flowers around the frame.

"I was living in Colorado," Jimmy continued, "and I went to college there. I was interested in engineering, and I just sat in on classes and seminars—they allow that—while I took any job I could get. I've worked as a short-order cook, bus boy, store detective, welder, chauffeur, all kinds of little

112

shit jobs. I was living in a college town and I was at that age when all my friends were in college. They were always hungry and struggling, and I was the cat that had the job. I was a truck driver, and I always had a pocketful of cash. But then I got into a thinking thing where, you know, I realized that now *I* had the pocketful of cash, but later on *they* would have the pocketful of cash and I would still be a truck driver. So I went to classes, maybe a semester. And with what I learned in classes, I worked my way into almost a mechanical engineer, you know, without any degree or any paper, cause I could do it. And that's what I did for about six years, job-wise, with a little hustlin on the side. Most I ever made workin was about ten thousand dollars, and that was with a lot of overtime."

The phone chimed again. "Yeah. Thirty minutes? Okay, what time is it now? You'll definitely be here in thirty minutes? Okay, bet to that."

He hung up and turned to me. "I got some business comin up. I'm gonna have to end this in about twenty minutes, okay?"

I nodded and checked my watch.

"So anyway, I got to playin football six or seven years ago. We had a good team, good equipment. I had my own equipment, the best you could buy. I always played defense, never wanted to play offense. I weighed one-ninety, too small to be a running back, but I never had a desire to run with the ball anyway. But I was fast. Like I could do the hundred in 9.5 or 9.6, and I liked to use my hands. To be offense, you present the challenge. To be defense, the challenge is presented *to you*. I dig that. I don't dig the idea of somebody being able to hit me and I can't do anything about it. It affects me. I don't like getting my ass broke. I'd much rather break the runner's ass, rather do the jamming than get jammed. And I knew I was tough out there. I was mean. Sometimes I thought I was meaner than I was.

"I remember one time I gave the coach some lip about something. And he said, 'Okay, you think you're bad, huh?' And he put me in at middle linebacker. Dig it! At 190 pounds. They ran three straight plays up the middle, and each time they wiped me out, really hurt me. And when they carried me off the field, I said wow, whooo! I'm not gonna give that coach any more word-for-word. I had to respect him.

"But I liked to hit them receivers, man, whew! We're running along, you know, dealin on a fly pattern, and I'll try to talk a fear thing into them: 'Put your hands in the air and I'm gonna bust your ass.' And you're the end or flanker or somethin, and you know the pill's comin, and you're gonna have to reach for it. And you know I'm there and gonna kick your ass. Hooo, man. Yeah, those were the good days, the good days."

I got up and put on my jacket. "Too bad you didn't make the pro team first," I said, "before you had the accident. That would have at least given you the satisfaction."

Jimmy looked at me with a pained expression. "Shit no. Oh no, man. That might have ruined my mind, might have wrecked me. I wanted to *play,* man. I wanted to play *football.* That's about the only thing I would say fuck hustlin for, if I could play some ball. Oh, I would still snort some coke and smoke some pot, but I wouldn't have tried to make money on it. I really wanted to play. And I wouldn't do any snortin *while* I was playin. You can't play and use drugs. When I play football it's one hundred percent. You can't do nothin throughout life half-ass. Half anything ain't worth shit.

"You see, you can take a snort of coke and you think in your mind that you're set up well for the game. Until somebody hits you, catches you correct, really busts your buns. Too much contact. You get hurt. You think you're making a fly move, but you are really out there fucking around, and

114

you get jacked up. Gotta be alert. Gotta really really really be thinking, man, gotta be. Can't have any delusions of grandeur out there, cause you'll get jammed."

He sat staring at his slippers, and when he heard the buzzer from the lobby door, he got up mechanically and went out to press the button which unlocked the door downstairs. He came back and sat down, jiggling his feet and looking at them. "I've run with a lot of professional football players," he said softly. "I know what I can do. I know what I *could* do. I know a lot of players come back from ankle injuries. I can't run. It hurts, man. If I try to sprint, after about thirty yards, tcheew! And I'm thirty now, over the hill. Probably if I could have played this year, I could play for six or seven more years, you know. But supposing I could come back, so what? What pro team wants to start tryin a guy who's thirty-one who is recovering from a bad ankle injury?"

His front doorbell rang, and he got up and went down the hall and opened all the locks. I heard some mumbling. Then he came back, rubbing his head, lips pressed together. "Oh shit man," he whispered. "You gotta get outta here. I forgot somebody was comin. Oh shit. Sorry."

He helped me gather up my pencils and paper and moved me out of the living room. He went ahead and tested the kitchen door to make sure it was shut, and gestured toward it. "Wheew!" he whispered. He opened the front door and pushed me gently through it. "Hey, I'm sorry to hustle you out. I didn't know no big motherfuckers were coming."

115

11

We walked in the clutter and clatter of Seventh Avenue, in the long shadows of late afternoon. Hookers and schoolgirls, junkies and businessmen, hustlers and college boys mixed together on the sidewalks. People, their voices obscured by the din of heavy traffic, chatted here and there on apartment stoops, in front of pool halls, restaurants, Black Panther offices, Chock Full-O'-Nuts, bars, storefront churches. It was the ambience that draws tourists to Harlem in closed buses.

Jimmy didn't like being with me on the street, though he made no protest. We just walked along, abreast but a few feet apart. He nodded occasionally to someone he knew, and would nod in the direction of someone whom he would identify to me, out of the corner of his mouth, as a hustler or pimp.

At the curb was a splendid black Ferrari, and I called his attention to it. "Mmm-mmm," he said, shaking his head. "*That* is a car, man. What do they go for, fifteen thousand or some shit? I'd love to have me one. But not here. I would want to *drive* the motherfucker."

We resumed our leisurely pace. "You're on the highway a lot," I said. "Why don't you get one?"

He shook his head. "See, what I'm doin, the image is important. Now, these cats on the street wouldn't have any idea what a car like that meant. They know what an El-dorado *means*. They can identify with it. But when I get me a fancy place out on the Island or someplace, where I can really drive, I'd like something like a Ferrari."

He nodded at an Eldorado stopped for a light. "See that car? That bubbletop? White tires? Fuckin nigger Cadillac. I wouldn't decorate my car, do all that shit to it, fuck up a good car and make it a nigger Cadillac. My car's got about all I want, good tape deck, extras, you know. I got me a TV I might put in it. I want to put a phone in it, but the telephone company will put you through a change now to do it. Got to find somebody to bribe. Or there's a couple private places I understand where you can go and buy one and shuffle it around that way. I spend a lot of time in that car. A telephone would save me a lot of time, man."

He looked again at the customized Eldorado. "That's a fuckin pimp drivin that car," he said. "I know him."

"You don't like pimps?" I said.

"Shit, I don't *talk* to pimps. Pimps as a rule don't have nothin to do with hustlers, and hustlers don't have nothin to do with pimps. You got to knock all those chicks in the face. They got to crawl to you. A guy just layin on his ass waitin for chicks to bring him bread—that's slimy, man. That's bullshit."

A man started across the street toward Jimmy. "Uh, I got to have a word with this hustler," he said. "Talk to you later, okay?"

"I think Jimmy always aspired to be a hustler," a friend said. "Even when he was nine-to-fiving. He had a reputation as a wild, mean, vicious son of a bitch. He was having trouble with his wife. She was a bitch. He used to haul her out of the bars and beat her ass—I mean fight her like he would fight *you*. Strange he stuck with that bitch as long as he did.

"I think at the time he had a couple of jobs, but he was lookin at being a hustler, and he started giving some thought

117

to being a pimp. This guy was going with a girl who had a roommate that was a hooker. I mean a real beautiful hooker with national experience. Well, Jimmy got onto that and he would go down to that apartment and—dig this—he would practically have *school* sessions on how to do it. Jimmy would ask questions on every aspect of being a pimp. We used to laugh about how he probed for information all the time, you know, the openness of it. After all, not every guy who wants to be a pimp says, 'How do you be a pimp?' You can't just learn to be a pimp. It has to come sort of natural to you. There's this whole love thing—almost a love-hate thing—that keeps the girls working for you. You can't even have 'lieutenants' like in the drug business, because it's essentially a one-to-one situation, the pimp and each of his girls. You have to be willing to kick their asses, I mean really kick their asses when they're sore, literally sore, from being abused. Jimmy is too nice a guy to beat up chicks."

Jimmy looked at me with narrowed eyes, and then at the floor. He sighed. "Yeah, we pimped a little, Slick and me. Slick and I been together a *long* time. We were nine-to-fivers together. I'm the violent type, and my partner is more rational, so we work well together.

"Yeah, we did a little pimpin. I had three or four girls. You know that girl you met up here the other day? She was one of them. She was in my stable. Wow, can she hook up! You saw how sweet she acted up here, how proper and all? That's because Phyl was here. She always acts different around Phyl, very proper, because Phyl doesn't dig any of that shit—although you may think she doesn't show it. Phyl can give you a word or a look that ices you."

He continued in a tone almost shy. "Pimpin is grimy. *I* think it is. It takes a special kind of cat to be a pimp. There's all kinds of hustlers—that term encompasses so many things —cause a cat that's a thief is a hustler. Cat that deals dope

118

is a hustler, you know, a dope merchant. All those cats are hustlers, terminology-wise. But pimps, now, pimps generally hang out with pimps, hustlers stay with hustlers. Pimps remind me of broads, the sho-nuff, sho-nuff pimps do. They're gaudy. Too many diamonds, too much flash. They need that kind of flash, but it's too much. You find that cats that beat broads usually don't fare too well with the male gender. But the best broad in the world after a while tries to get slick, put something aside for herself. Catch her doin that, you gotta break her hands.

"I didn't like beatin chicks. But I did. You got to. That broad that was up here? I had to beat her one time. You beat them with a wet towel to leave no marks. It's all built around a love thing, you know. They all want *you*. The girls get nothin, no money. They get a wardrobe and shit. But you know what it is? Every one of them hopes to end up as your girl and marry you and have a house and shit. They don't mind sharing you because each one has that hope."

"How do you make them love you?" I asked artlessly.

He snorted and gave a weak, crooked smile. "That's easy. They liked me because I was icy. Some chicks that have hooked for me, I wouldn't even touch them until they earned it."

He sighed and leaned back, putting his hands behind his head. "So anyway, I began to put it aside, you know, and this girl you met got a love thing goin with a cat, and that's where it's at now with her."

He closed his eyes and rubbed his hands down his face. "Yeah, pimpin is grimy. I made some good money with it, but shit . . ."

Jimmy set his hustling style early. When he was in the streets selling reefer and a little cocaine, one of his friends was living in a high-rent building on Riverside Drive where lived some prominent entertainers.

"Jimmy was supplying me with a little stuff," the friend

119

recalled, "and one time I was giving a party, so I asked him to deliver a little product. I had the place all set up nice, with just candlelight. And Jimmy walks in and stops dead. He's got his hand in his coat, like fucking Napoleon. Right away he demands that all the lights be turned on. I damn near couldn't keep from laughing, but he was serious. He eyed everybody with that tough, suspicious look of his, you know, wouldn't even sit down. And I said, 'Hey Jim, cut out the Cagney bit. These people are all okay. They're my *friends*.' And then I forgot that Jimmy doesn't smoke or drink, and I offered him a drink. And he straightened up, you know, like I'd said a shocking thing. And he said, 'Don't you know the dealer doesn't drink? Clouds the mind.' "

The friend shook his head and chuckled at the memory. "Jimmy was running like crazy just trying to make a dollar," he said. "And we had this really hip doorman who used to supply everybody in the building with whatever they used. So I suggested to Jimmy that if he could supply that doorman, and maybe a few others, he could make some good bread, and wouldn't even have to work the street anymore. So we set up a meet, but Jimmy couldn't make it. That happened a few times, you know—like with you and him in the beginning. He never could make it, for one reason or another, and I couldn't figure it out. So finally I pressed him on it, and it turned out that the fucker knew about all the fly people living in that building and he wouldn't come around until he could do it in style, with all his diamonds flashing."

The friend knitted his brow and looked intently at me. "You know what? I think all this came back to me because of how he kept putting you off about visiting the stash. Did it ever occur to you that it might have been because his stash wasn't big and impressive enough at the time?"

"Mistakes?" Jimmy said with a stony look. "Sure I made mistakes. But I been learning a long time. Look, when my

120

mom was around, and I was about eleven, she was so tough about me not starting on anything, you know. She was gonna beat me if I started on reefer or some shit. But that just made me want to see the man so bad, just because she made him sound so tough. I wanted to see him in the school-yard."

He did see him in the schoolyard, so to speak. He started smoking marijuana when he was eleven, buying it from other kids at school. "Like that's the way it's done, man. You don't have none of this evil man coming up to school kids and saying, 'Hey, here, try some of my product.' That's not the way it's done with *any* drugs. You buy some because you dig it. And I dug it—hey! But I couldn't afford it. So I had to get a thing going, and so I began to split to friends so I could smoke for free. Then maybe you tell your friends how to split to *their* friends, and you got a thing going."

An ounce, then, may have cost fifteen or twenty dollars. In Harlem you can sell a joint for a dollar. There are forty or fifty joints in an ounce. So if you sell twenty joints, you have half an ounce left for yourself, at no cost.

"You know what?" Jimmy said. "Reefer should cost a hundred dollars a pound, or one-ten maximum. At least that's what it used to cost when I was a kid. When I was fourteen or fifteen I'd get down with four or five guys and we had little bullshit jobs and everybody would put in fifteen or twenty dollars apiece and we'd get a pound of reefer.

Jimmy opened his green canister and rolled a couple more joints from his dwindling supply of Calif. He lit one and leaned back to savor the first puff.

"When I was sixteen I bought my first twenty-dollar cap of coke. Two friends of mine had given me five dollars apiece to get them some coke, and a five-dollar blow is not quite a quarter of a twenty-dollar cap. So I gave each of them theirs, which left me a little more than half, and gave me half my investment back. Next day another fellow came to me and wanted ten dollars' worth of coke, and I sold it to him. Upon doing that I realized I had sold twenty dollars' worth of coke, got my whole investment back, and still had a little blow for myself."

"But you weren't dealing when you were sixteen?" I said.

"No, but what I'm telling you is that I've been learning for a long time. As a kid I knew how things worked. By the time I decided to be a full-time hustler, I knew a lot and I had contacts. But sure I made mistakes—not a lot, but some. Overcutting, for example. You know, you fuck with somebody, put in too much cut. You may not get hurt, but the fellow will want his money back. You lose it, simple as that. So you learn it doesn't pay to fuck people around.

"Then there's trusting people, letting money be owed to you. Shit, I just recently learned to say no. If I had learned to say no earlier, I wouldn't be owed what I am owed, which is too much. My partner *still* doesn't know how to say no. I'm not saying he won't *hurt* you, but he's a softy in some ways.

"And then you can worry about the PO-lice too much, throw coke away. You're walkin down the street, a police car comes up and slows down, and you throw your coke into the street. Then the car keeps goin, and you say, oh shit! I threw my coke away for nothin. That's happened to me. Not anymore. I got to know they're coming for me before I throw my thing away. And even then I may not. They can stop and talk to me now. I ain't throwing my thing away."

12

"I hope they legalize reefer myself," Jimmy said, smoking his third joint of the morning. "I hope they legalize it, cause I'm a *user,* baby. I'm addicted. I dig reefer. Oh man! Reefer and coke, that's my thing."

He held the joint under his nose and inhaled the smoke.

"But you've still got an operation going with reefer," I said.

"Hey, heh-heh. Shit yeah. Long as it pays. I have a lot of housewives, welfare broads, that move smoke for me. And it's a nice thing, brings me a nice piece of money. One time I was uptight financially, and without that I might really have been jammed. But you got eleven or twelve broads givin you from twenty-five to fifty dollars a day, or every other day anyway, it'll help you over the rough spots."

"Where do you get your grass?"

"Oh, a lot of places. I have a lot of people I deal with for reefer. Mainly what I like to do, what I try to do, is go get it myself. I've done it a few times. One time down in Panama, twice I was in the West Indies, Puerto Rico. There's a lot of places you can bring it back from."

"Is it easy to buy good grass down there?"

"You have to have a connection, same as here. Can't just walk around the street and ask for grass, not in weight. It's dangerous. And also you'll be taken advantage of, unless you know somebody. So I have bought it and then brought it in, right through Kennedy International Airport. You know that Calif I had around for a while? I brought that in. A hundred pounds. You know how? Hey."

Jimmy stood up and narrowed his eyes and snapped his fingers and described how, during the Great Marijuana Famine in the summer of 1969, when federal authorities were cracking down mightily at the borders, he had disguised himself and his mission.

"Yeah," he said. "That was *then*. I just looked tired-ass. I'm just comin home, baby"—snap, snap—"I'm hip, but not a hippie. They couldn't see the forest for the trees. All you have to do is need a shave, smell kind of musty, and hook up like I did. And, heh-heh, you might say I made a slight profit on that reefer, hmmm?"

He sat down. "Yeah, that was cool. But I wouldn't possibly try it today. They've really tightened up. I wouldn't try it, not me. I look around for other places."

"Did you ever get burned on bad reefer?"

"You mean fake reefer? Hell no. When I was a kid there was no such thing as fake reefer. Now there's all kinds of shit. I've bought reefer that wasn't the quality I thought it was when I bought it, but I've never bought some that was complete fake—nooo. You got to be a go-fer to do some shit like that. If somebody sold me some shit like that, you know what they'd have to do?" He laughed. "They'd have to leave town."

"A lot of people," I said, "claim they can tell the quality of reefer by its color or smell or texture or something. Can you do that?"

"Look at it and tell? That's impossible. That's bullshit. Don't believe that. Now, look at this." He opened his green canister and picked up some marijuana with his fingers and let it sprinkle back down. "Now that looks like good reefer, if you imagined how good reefer looks. But that doesn't necessarily mean anything, cause I can go out in the kitchen and get something and grind it up and it will look just like that. Now, some people will look at this and say, 'Man, that's nothing, cause the coloring is so light and it don't look like nothin but a little oregano.' But we know what it is, right?"

He leaned over to me and lowered his voice as if to be confidential.

"Hey, one time I had some reefer that smelled like cow do-do. Goddamn did it stink! And it was gray, looked mildewed. Awful terrible-looking. It even had a nasty foul taste to it. And my friend, it would *wreck* you. It would topple you over. Oooh, hey! It was a smoker. It was some of the best I ever had, but it looked like garbage. The proof of the pudding is in the eating, man, you got to taste it, smoke it. That's the only way you'll really really know. Unless you're a chemist and you can test it for the cannabis content and shit like that."

"You charged thirty-five dollars an ounce for that Calif."

"Yeah."

"That seems high, even for good grass. Are prices higher around here than in the white market?"

"Yeah. Sure. You can probably get the same stuff cheaper there than here. That's because there are more of you than there are of us. Calif that I would sell for thirty-five dollars might be twenty-five down in Greenwich Village. The whole business of bringing it in and so forth, you dudes can do that easier than black cats. And hey, shit. Everything costs more in Harlem, man. Harlem has inflation *all* the time. But then again down in the Village it's very risky to buy drugs. You can get burned, Goddamn you can get burned. Like someone gives you a joint and says, 'Sample that,' and oh boy, it's dynamite. Okay. Here's twenty-five dollars, give me an ounce. And you buy it and you take it home and try it and find out that you smoked one good reefer for free and bought an ounce of Central Park grass for twenty-five dollars. It's the same old thing: How reliable is the supplier? It costs *me* more up here, so I have to charge more. But you get, you know—well, you know, right?"

"You also sell smaller amounts up here," I said.

"Sure. Just like with coke, the biggest money is in the smallest amounts, if you could move it just as fast. A pound of reefer costs me $125–$150. I sell it to you for two hundred. If you took that same pound and sold ounces for twenty-five dollars—sixteen times twenty-five is four hundred, right? You double your money. Now, you take those ounces and you break them up into five-dollar bags. There's six or seven five-dollar bags in an ounce. Then, if you roll joints, there's between ten and fifteen joints in a five-dollar bag. So you take a pound of reefer and joint it up, that two hundred dollars will be worth about a thousand, because a joint is a dollar. The catch is, how long will it take? But oooh, that would be boss if you could do it like that"— snap.

"Why would anybody pay a dollar for a single joint?"

"Well, a bag costs five dollars, and you only got three dollars. You can't get a bag, but you want to get high and go to the movies, right? Movie costs a dollar and a half. You can buy a joint and some popcorn."

Jimmy sighed and leaned back and relit his joint. "Oh yeah, there's a lot of different smokes, all different kinds of highs. There's angel dust—that's parsley dipped in acid. That's a high. There's hash, which I love, but good hash is harder to get than coke, around here anyway. Hash is a different high. Sometimes it gives me an upset stomach or a headache. You can mix hash with reefer, and then you get a hash-and-reefer high, which is different again. I like to mix hash with cigarette tobacco. That's nice, smooth, right? Hey, I've had hash that was dipped in opium—whew! That will take your head off."

He yawned and bobbed his head to a record of the Four Tops. "Yeah, the Calif is gone. But there is some other stuff around."

He looked at me with a conspiratorial grin. Then he took from his pocket a tiny manila envelope about the width and length of a cigarette pack. More carefully than usual he sprinkled some of the contents into the double cigarette paper. He also sprinkled less than usual. Jimmy usually rolls thick joints. "You got to put some *reefer* in it," he will say to someone who is rolling one of normal width. But now he was rolling a very slender joint, hardly thicker than a pipe cleaner.

"This," he said, holding it daintily in front of him between his thumb and forefinger, "is the best reefer I have ever tasted. I mean *ever* tasted, and heh-heh, I've been into some reefer in my time. I use this very sparingly, very sparingly. Listen: First time I tried this, I lit up a joint, you know, driving along in my car. And in about thirty-five seconds *I had to pull my car over to the side!* Can you dig what I'm saying? I have never had to pull my car over to the side for no drug. And you know what?" He gritted his teeth. "I can't buy this. It's Colombian smoke. The man who's got it won't sell any weight. Like he'll sell me a five-dollar bag, but he'll only sell five-dollar bags." He slapped the little envelope down on the table, at the same time making sure nothing spilled. "He won't sell me half a pound. One of those little faggots that, you know, he's got a good thing and he don't want to share it with n-o-b-o-d-y. He wants it all. But I got to get me some. *Got* to."

Jimmy's smile became satanic. "And you know what? I'm ready to stick him up to do it. I'm gonna find a way to make that motherfucker give me some. I got to set him up. I'm serious. Put some friends on him. Hey, have you ever heard of the Murphy game? You know what the Murphy is on the street? Somebody walks up and flashes a badge, and he is not the police, and he takes you off. That's called the Murphy. That motherfucker don't sell me some reefer, I'm gonna take it off him."

A deep laugh filled the apartment of a friend of Jimmy's named Herbie. "Hey, you know what?" he said, still laughing. "That's probably *my* weed he's talking about. I'll bet that's what it is, except that mine is Jamaican—but he would probably hide that fact too. He really loves to talk, doesn't he? Even with all that bullshit, he's okay. He's just funny about some things. Like I owe him a piece of change —three or four hundred dollars. But I'm not going to give him all of it, because he's been shorting me a little bit— you know, supposed to be selling me a pound and it's a couple ounces under, shit like that, doesn't mean more than a couple of dollars, and I'm a *friend* of his, you know. It's like he's always got to be hustling a little bit, always got to be on top of you. On the other hand, you get a situation like, one time he was really jammed on cash. I think he needed some right away to buy some coke or something. But in any case he was anxious. So he wanted to sell me a pound of reefer—nothing special, so-so reefer. I told him I would buy it, but I couldn't come and pick it up. He was so anxious for the cash that he brought it over. Now, I happened to know that he paid $125 for it, and you would expect him to name his price, you know. So I said, 'How much?' And he just shrugged and said, 'What can I get?' And I just took a shot and said $125. And he just shrugged again and took it. Now, can you imagine Jimmy taking that?"

"Hard to," I said. "How's he going to react when you don't pay him all you owe?"

"Well shit, you know, I got to keep him a little straight, so I'll just tell him to his face that I know he's been fuckin me a little and I'm paying him fairly for what I got. Oh, then he might try to lay a little hint of a threat on me, like he might say, 'You sure you know what you're doin?' But it won't mean nothin.

"But I'll tell you something. He's not exaggerating about that reefer, if it's mine he's talking about. But shit, I'll sell him all he wants, at *cost*. He knows that. What is probably bothering him is that I won't introduce him to the guy that sells it to *me* so that he can get his own thing going with it. Fuckin Jimmy. He can't stand it when somebody else has got something *he* doesn't have. Like some cat will have a long Afro, and Jimmy will wish his own would grow faster. Or I'll have on a pair of new boots that he will dig, and tomorrow he will show up with a new pair of even fancier boots. He's a trip."

Herbie put a reefer on the arm of the chair in which I was sitting. "That's it. Try it. I'm not gonna smoke just now, because I'm going out later. But you go ahead."

I lit up.

"I tell you," he said, "Jimmy wasn't kidding about that reefer. You might want to smoke just half of it."

"*Half* of it?" I said, mindful of the fact that we groovies who populate the tall, sleek buildings of midtown may, on occasion, smoke three or four joints in an evening. "Are you kidding?"

"Nope," he said as he went out of the room.

I took a deep drag, and then another. On the third drag I felt a tingle in my toes, as if they were reviving from the cold. After a couple more puffs I went to the bathroom and delivered a piss of extraordinary duration. Then I came back to the living room and sat down. Herbie beckoned to me.

"Come in here," he said, pointing to the bedroom. "I want you to really experience something."

I went docilely in and he put his hands on my shoulders to seat me on the edge of the bed, and then he planted earphones on me and installed a stack of records on the turntable and carefully adjusted the sound.

"Just relax and enjoy it," he said, taking the remaining roach of the joint from my fingers.

I am already covered by a general wooze as the first record drops down. It is a voice I know well, a song I know, but my recollective connections won't close. "Who's the singer?" I ask as the tones pound into my head.

"Aretha Franklin, man."

I am embarrassed. Things are going on. If a white man is cool in a black man's pad, he knows when Aretha is on. What the hell is the matter with me? I don't believe it! I look around for Herbie. He's in the other room. I want to call him, but I don't. Hooo, man, the sounds are strong. Not loud, but they have a curious power. What is that power? Now I know. I am anticipating the sounds, the notes. It is the difference between the first time with sex and later times, when you know what is coming and you're ready for it and the anticipation builds it and over you go in the wave and pow! But something is missing because this doesn't end. Power, power, driving power of the music that gets so strong I think my head is lighting up and I have to take the earphones off and lie back on the bed. Whew! What the hell is going on? Where the hell is Herbie? Hey Herbie? But I know that stays in my head with the rest and I haven't really called him. But I want to tell him that this is crazy. I get up off the bed and go to the living-room door and look in. And there he is, talking on the telephone. Shshshsh. You can't disturb a guy on his own telephone. But there's something worse. I'm embarrassed. Suppose he saw me peek around the doorjamb and he thinks I'm listening? I go back to the bed and sit down and put on the earphones. Hey, is that the same song? The same song still? How the hell long is a song? How the hell long, dum-dum-dum, is a long long song? On and on and on the song. I don't believe it! What is it that stack of records looks like? Just records. Got to tell Herbie I don't believe it. Got to find out what the hell is going on. He is still on the telephone. What is he setting up? Is he setting me up? He's not setting up anything, you dumb bastard. He's a friend. He's a black friend. Oh-oh. Something I don't like is creeping into my head. He's a black friend. He knows I am white. Why the hell is he being so

130

nice to me? What is he saying to somebody on the phone?
Dumb white motherfucker in there in my bedroom out of
control. Of course he's not saying that. Dumb white motherfucker messing around up here, thinking he's cool, thinking
he knows something about drugs, thinking he's tough. Shit,
I could break the motherfucker in two with one hand. Out
of control on one joint. Wheew! Damn music. So strong I
want to cry. It actually hurts my stomach. High-pitched
sounds like Swedish chimes. Swedish chimes! What the hell
are Swedish chimes, you white prick. I hate that word. Or
do I hate that thought, about that word? Don't think about it
at all then. I can actually see the sounds running up and
down my vertebrae. No, that's not the truth. That's a cliché.
That's not what I really see. The typewriter I took apart yesterday and couldn't fix, there is a row of teeth along the
bottom of the carriage. That is what I see the sounds running on, skittering along, tickling. Wrong word. Typewriters
don't tickle, you fake writer. People laugh at writers who
use wrong metaphors. I am embarrassed, but nobody is going to laugh because nobody is in here with me to hear what
I am thinking. Is there? Oh for Christsake, be *honest*. That's
what it really looks like. What's that! There is a full-length
mirror on the closet door in the hallway outside the bedroom. Herbie is just walking by, that's all, in the mirror.
Herbie. Herbie!

"Yeah, man?"

"I don't believe it."

"Hey, man, heh-heh-heh, ha-ha-ha. Just relax, man."

"I'm embarrassed."

"Don't be embarrassed, man. We all go through it."

"I feel crazy."

He taps me on the arm and laughs and goes out, through
the mirror. I clasp my hands together and hold them tightly
between my knees and pull my shoulders together and smile
because the music makes me do it. I am all pulled together.

131

Wow! I look down, and it is far down to the street. Way down. No people down there because there wouldn't be any people on the red carpet below the bed. What the hell is wrong with my body! My body is all humped up down there, separated from where I am, all humped up in a ball. No it's not. Take those earphones off! I lie back on the bed. I forgot to take the earphones off! Oh my God I probably broke the cord. No I didn't. It's still together. All those curls for expansion. Shit, it can stretch a long way. Wonder how far. Probably from here to . . . Whew! But I want to take them off and walk around. I'm trapped in the damn cord. It's all twisted around my leg. No it's not. It's just lying there across the floor plugged into the hi-fi. I can pick it up. It's not twisted around anything. I can take the earphones off. Sure I can. Why the hell don't I? Okay, I do. But I put them right back on again. Enjoy it! What's that in the mirror? In the corner of my eye because I don't turn my head? Herbie. What the hell is Herbie doing? He's just combing his Afro. He's got his shirt off. Jesus! I hope to hell I don't have to take *my* shirt off. I don't want him to see *me* that way. Hold it. He's not there anymore. Now I can turn my head and make sure. He's talking to somebody in the living room. Who? Who? Who? What the hell's he doing, bringing people in here to see me like this? To laugh? There's nobody in the living room. He's talking on the phone. Hey, man, have you forgotten just who the hell you are? And what the hell you're doing? These cats you're dealing with can't just be bringing people around. You are too fucking dangerous. You can hang the whole bunch of them if you want to. Jesus Christ! Did I *say* that? That's not something you say, man, even if you think it. Sounds like a threat. Christ I hope I didn't say it. I got to talk to somebody. I am so lonely. This is crazy. There are people everywhere I could talk to. Telephone right beside me. Call somebody. Oh shit, Herbie's on the phone, right? Or even if he's not, I can't just

132

be picking up the phone when he doesn't know about it and calling somebody. Who the hell you calling, man, who the hell you tipping off? Everything is so *complicated*. These are just weird thoughts, but I don't want all these thoughts, because thoughts are fucking *real*. I am laughing at that, because suddenly it is a funny idea about thoughts, that you can't really do anything about them, like you can't tell them to beat it. I go to the window and look out. A block away stand two police cars and several policemen because that is where Manhattan District Attorney Frank Hogan lives. Now, that is insane. There are so many things I want to remember to tell Herbie.

"I got to go out for a few minutes, just to get some cigarettes."

Herbie! I got to talk to Herbie. I got to hold on to him and talk.

"It's just down to the corner. Be gone about five minutes, if the phone should ring."

"Fine. See you in five minutes."

"Relax."

"I feel fantastic, but I don't believe it."

What does it mean, his smile? He is putting on a white coat in front of the mirror, over a flowered shirt and red bell-bottom pants. Why is he doing all that primping to go to the corner for a pack of cigarettes? Is it because—oh shit!—he's black? I am wearing dungarees. I am wearing expensive boots and dungaree pants and a dungaree shirt and a dungaree jacket and my hair is long and hip. I am a pretty cool-looking guy this way. I think I'll call somebody and tell them where I am and what I'm into and blow their minds and impress the shit out of them. Oh shit no. Got to be careful. Don't even call home. No point in worrying anybody. Pretty Goddamn responsible, I am. I am cool. I take off the earphones and get up and walk over to the mirror to look at my cool self. What the hell is wrong? I am funny-looking and misshapen. I am all crooked and pale and dumpy and messy, and *funny-looking!* My shoulders are narrow and my hips are broad and fat and my hands are gnarled up. I try to pull my jacket down hard on one side to straighten my body. I turn away because I am really scared to look like that. Come on, I don't look like that, not that bad. Be reasonable. Some chicks dig me and I have a beautiful wife who maybe doesn't know how I look. I don't look like that. Not all crooked. I look into the mirror again. I look normal. I look for a long time. I am afraid to move because I might slip out of shape again. I stay normal. Whew! But time is so long. The clock doesn't move. It takes an hour to move five minutes. Exactly an hour. Somebody is at the door! I run back into the bedroom and sit down and put on the earphones. Herbie comes in and passes the mirror without looking at me. Was he there all the time, watching? Now this is really ridiculous. I am pacing around the bedroom. I am stuck in the bedroom. I am looking at things and touching things in *his* bedroom. Things on his dresser top. Cocaine spread out on aluminum foil. A package of Kools and I giggle because I have not read it before. Warning: The Surgeon General Has Determined That Cigarette Smoking Is Dangerous to Your Health. Wallet, handkerchief, Afro comb—*wallet!* There is a five-dollar bill on top of his wallet. What if I took it? What if I *took* it! White man in a black man's apartment and he takes five dollars off the dresser! That's what a *black* man does in a *white* man's apartment. Why you bigoted motherfucker. White bigoted faggot bastard thief! Nonsense. I'm not stealing five dollars. I've never stolen five dollars in my life. *But suppose I can't help it?* Oh shit, get away from the dresser. Way away. Into the corner. Crouch down and hide. Really hide behind the bed and away from the dresser where Herbie can't see me. Can't *see* me? Of course he can see me. You can't hide in the corner of a man's bedroom. I don't believe what is going on. Herbie? Herbie? Herbie!

"Yeah, man."

"I was hiding."

He is smiling, but it is okay. "What you mean, hiding?"

"Hey, Herbie, I don't believe it. I am going crazy. I am not coming down. What the hell is it you gave me?"

He is laughing, but it is okay. He is my friend. It is okay.

"Yeah, that's something, isn't it? I told you you might want to try half a joint first."

"It can't be grass. Grass doesn't bother me. Grass makes me sleepy. Is there something in it?"

"No man, just grass. Just this stuff here."

He picks up a brown paper bag full of weeds and branches. "Just this. You mean is it soaked in something? No, no. Shit, man, relax. I have had this stuff. I know what it can do."

"Does this happen to you, what is happening to me?"

"Not anymore. But I can dig it, you know. See, I really think it has something to do with being a creative person, you know, your pores are more open to things, you're more receptive to imagination and senses and all."

"But grass doesn't . . ."

"And there's another thing which I think I understand. You're in a place where, you know, you don't really feel at ease, deep down. I can dig how that comes out. Hey, just relax and enjoy it. Relax. You know what will bring you down? A one-and-one will bring you right down. Just take a one-and-one if you want to."

He is gone, and things are easing up. I'm just sitting here breathing hard. But it's coming back. Oh man, I want to take a one-and-one. But I can't. Maybe it's *meant* that I go through this. I am hungry. Oh I am so hungry that I am scared. I am panicked. I got to have something to eat. Maybe it's *meant* that I don't have anything to eat. Oh God if I don't come down and I don't ever eat. So hungry. Now I can feel it, really *feel* it: This must be something like what it is to be crazy, to be so hungry when you could eat and be

135

so lonely when there are people around. I am not going crazy, of course. Does a person know when he is going crazy? I am so lonely I want to cry. Herbie is right there, but I am inside of me and locked in and even talking to him is not me. And I am tired. I can't get down, and it has been hours. I know I will have to write this tonight or tomorrow and I am so tired. Too tired to write it down ever, but I know I will have to write it down because it is the strongest experience of my life. Why do I have to feel *guilty* about it? Same old guilt, about not working, about not working *now,* and hungry and tired and lonely. Ow! Something hit me. A football. Hi, Sammy.

"Hi, Richard. You want to see me hit the line?"

"Sure."

Sammy takes the football and slams into the bed, and I am laughing. I am feeling better, maybe coming down. He throws me the ball and I throw it back. Now Sammy is dancing. Sammy is snapping his fingers and sliding his head back and forth and moving his hips and shuffling his feet in a dance that only black people can do and he is only seven so how the hell can he do it already?

"You're a good dancer, Sammy."

He is dancing harder, smiling, showing me, singing with the words on the record. He has stopped.

"Don't stop, Sammy, don't stop. Please dance some more. I like to see you dance. How did you learn that, what makes you dance like that?"

Oh shit, watch it. Don't come to Harlem to watch smiling black niggers shuffle and stomp. He is gone. Now I can't resist dancing. I hope to hell nobody is watching, but I don't really give a shit, because this is so important. I feel like I am *dancing black*. I feel like my head is moving in that peculiar serpentine way, and my feet. You know what? I bet that inside every white man there is a little black man trying to get out.

"Beautiful, man." Herbie slaps my palms because he likes what I have said. He has not seen me dance. I am explaining how I feel. But he's gone again, and the loneliness is back, and the hunger, deep and so dark. I could just go out to a restaurant. I could just take a one-and-one. I could call somebody. Hey Sammy. Would you bring me a cracker or a piece of bread or something?

"Hey, man, if you're hungry, just help yourself to anything in the refrigerator. There's probably not a whole hell of a lot in there, but take whatever you can find. I'm not going to eat anyway."

"Okay, Herbie."

Herbie has come into the bedroom with a book about marijuana. He is thumbing through it. "I know this can happen. This is a good book. Trips like this are described in here, just from weed. Look through it if you feel like it."

"Thanks."

He is not wearing a shirt again, and I like the way he looks. Broad shoulders and muscles. Or is it that I don't like the way *I* look? Is it faggy to dig a strong male body? Is it possible to become a fag by just worrying about it? What do I do about *that?* Oh you dumb shit. What is all this shit about *maleness?* Nobody's a fag. You're just a soft white man in a hard black man's house, that's all. If you can go crazy just by thinking about it, why can't you come down just by thinking about it?

"Hey Herbie." I am laughing like hell and sliding off the bed.

"Yeah man?"

"I don't believe all this."

He is laughing too. "Relax."

He is laughing, and he slaps my palms and goes out. *How long can this go on?* Now the bedroom is all strange images. The bedspread is crumpled on the floor, and one of my *shoes* is on it! I am standing on the bedspread, which is a

137

dirty pig thing to do, and I jump off. A tiny blue light in the amplifier suddenly explodes. A tangle of clothes by the bed is football shoulderpads. Crazy, one after another. There is a chopstick on the floor and I am anxious to see what it really is, so I move it with my foot. It is really a chopstick. I lie back on the bed and have *déjà vu* about the light fixture which has one bulb and one empty socket. When I was a kid. I am wincing at the pain of recall. I don't know why, can't make it. But I am giggling. I am crawling on the bed. I am sneaking up on the grass book *like a cat*. A happy cat. I reach out with a paw and toy with the book. I can't stop laughing. But the clock. Why won't time go by? Time is staying the same! It will take me too long to come down! It will be too late! I am terrified. I have to eat. Herbie is on the telephone and mustn't be disturbed. I am proud of my act of will which draws my body up and propels me to the kitchen and makes me open the refrigerator. It's survival, Goddamnit! There is some cheese and some bread and a piece of fried chicken. Okay. Two kinds of cheese. Okay. I will eat a piece of that kind of cheese of which there is more, so Herbie will have plenty left. The pieces are the same size! There is not much bread left. Maybe Herbie will want a sandwich. There is only one piece of chicken. I have never known such despair. I close the refrigerator and return to the bedroom. I realize now that I am filled with both exhaustion and terror because I am utterly unable to help myself. I must ride it through, whatever. It is a long time before I go into the living room. Herbie is sitting on the sofa, watching television. I sit in the chair next to him.

"Herbie, I am so tired. I was so scared, so lonely."

"I can dig it. Hey man, your head was open."

"But Herbie, coke never does anything *close* to that. I mean, coke doesn't make you feel crazy at all. And I felt crazy on that grass."

"I'm hip, man. Coke will open you up, but good grass

can put you away. It happens, I know. Certain times. Certain situations. You might take a joint of this same stuff tomorrow and just a nice easy high. You might never go through anything like this again. It's happened to me."

Herbie reaches over and taps my arm. "Listen man, don't worry about it. I think you need to relax. There's a Chinese restaurant on the corner. Go get yourself something to eat. Talk to you tomorrow. We're gonna be friends for a long, long time."

Time has, after all, passed. I smoked the joint at seven o'clock. It is now eleven. The Chinese restaurant is closed. But I can go home and eat. Now I can.

13

"Hey, come on in. Something I want to show you."

Jimmy padded briskly ahead toward the bedroom. He was wearing black bell-bottom trousers and a wide leather belt. In a minute he was back in the living room, cradling in his arms against his bare black chest a tiny golden bundle of dog, a pup all hair, with nubs for legs, its face obscured by what appeared to be a beard which grew out of the top of its head and covered its whole body.

"Yorkshire terrier," Jimmy said, beaming, rubbing the dog's head. "His name is Jocko." He put Jocko down, and Jocko cringed where he was put. "Best little dog you can get. I'm gonna train him and enter him in some shows."

I couldn't help laughing, and Jimmy smiled in pleasure at my delight. "What I really want," he said, "is a German police dog, as I told you. But I can't keep him in an apartment. I like this one for the house. I was gonna get a poodle, but they're too nervous and don't make as good a pet. The best pet you can have in the family of miniature dogs is a Yorkshire terrier, and they're also the most expensive."

"How much?" I asked, running my fingers through Jocko's beard.

"Guess."

"Couple hundred dollars?"

"Three hundred and fifty dollars," he said, carefully stressing each syllable. "Got him from the best shop, took him to the best vet. Hey, I have never had a dog before.

Never had a pet of any kind. Now I have a little dog, and I love him. I dig him really."

Jocko was sniffing the rug, but not moving from the spot where he had been deposited. Jimmy went out and returned with an armload of a small circular inflatable dog bed, brushes, combs, rubber bones, and a book on Yorkshire terriers.

"He's three months old. You shouldn't get them any younger than that. He's not housebroken or anything. You have to comb and brush him three times a day to keep his coat nice."

He picked Jocko up and nuzzled him nose to nose. "Hey Jocko, ol' badness. Bwess yo wittow sewf." Then he put the dog down again. "And hey! He can run, whew! He really thinks he's superfly when he gets into his thing. All the cats I know wanna see him. I been ravin about him. Phyl won't let me take him out yet. But all the cats, you know, 'Hey Jim, when you gonna bring him down to the bar?' "

"Wow," I said. "Take him to the bar? That might raise some eyebrows."

Jimmy raised his. "About me being a faggot? Bet to that. Nobody who knows me is going to think that. And nobody who doesn't know me is going to say it. It wouldn't bother me because I don't have no doubts about my masculinity. I don't have to prove myself to the world." He laughed. "How many other black hustlers got a Yorkshire terrier?"

He motioned for me to follow him into the bedroom, where he wanted to finish dressing.

"Understand you had quite a trip the other day," he said over his shoulder.

"Yeah."

"Well, I wouldn't have left you alone," he said.

"What do you mean?"

He shrugged. "I just mean, like, you made it clear it was goin bad. I would have talked you back."

"Herbie was there," I said, "just in the other room."

He looked at me. "I mean I wouldn't have left your *side,* man." He turned to his closet.

"Any word from B.J.?" I asked.

"He's all right. He's in solitary just now. Some fuckin guard heard about B.J. knowing karate or some shit, and I guess the guard knew a little too, and the guard just taunted him and taunted him until—well, B.J. don't taunt too tough. I understand he put a little somethin on the guard."

"That *really* jams him up now, I guess," I said.

"Naw. He'll be out soon. I can imagine they don't want him around there anyway. He'll be back." He held up for appraisal a new black leather suit from France, then put it back in the closet.

"With B.J. gone," I said, "does anybody try to push you around on the street?"

He cocked his head and looked at me. "Hey now. B.J. helps me, but he don't hold me up. You got to handle most things yourself anyway. Ain't nobody can handle your money *or* yourself but *you.*

"Like the other day I was in a joint, and here's some fuckin creep. I don't even know this guy. But he knows *of* me. Pool game. Now, there's no money in that. We were just shooting a game of pool and I beat him. And he says to me, 'I'm gonna put my feet in your chest.' So I had to threaten to kill him. It's weird, because I would have blown his head off, cause he was leanin on me. It really got ultra-intense, cause when his mouth started goin, I had to take it to the max. See, he wanted to test me, see what he could do. The pool game was just the vehicle that was used. So he threatened to put his feet in my chest. You can't just walk away from that. Or else he might try it, then or some other time. He apologized and shit, and by making him cow down and apologize, he knows he better not try it. But even more important, so does everybody else in the bar. Now that's the kind of thing you got to handle yourself."

For some reason I was reminded of an incident several years ago when I stood in a ring of black and white on-lookers while two small teen-age boys, one black and one white, fought. The two, while both undersized for their age, were of equal size. The white boy was on top, in seeming red-faced command. The black boy gritted his teeth and steadfastly refused to surrender. Suddenly the white boy, who was winning, seemed to panic, and quit. A bigger black boy, standing next to me, spat on the ground. "That's the trouble with white people," he said. "They're afraid to *fight*."

Perhaps the memory was reawakened in relation to Jimmy because—if it is not too grand a notion—so many matters of status seem to be determined less by conquest than by willingness to engage.

Jimmy held up a dark gold shirt over his chest, then rejected it and hung it back up.

"Do you have a lot of friends on the street?" I asked.

"Nope. But I have a lot of people that respect me. Because I'm fair. Like the man said, when you can walk with kings and still not lose the common touch . . ."

"Are you always fair?"

"Well, I can rap, you know. I'm not above standin on the corner with a junkie listenin to his problems, if I know him.

"But see, there's always somebody watching, you know— just how tough are you, just how together are you. And there's cats that dislike me, because of jealousy, cats that talk about me, and I hear it. But they're talkin behind my back, and then when they see me it's: 'Hey baby, how you doin?' All that friendly shit. But if I hear from a reliable source that somethin is bein said about me I'll slowly ice the dude that's the cause of it."

Jimmy spun around and dropped the shirt he was holding. "There's this one dude sayin—now dig this"—Jimmy

143

affected a stern, deep voice and thrust out his lips—" 'That motherfucker Jimmy ain't nothin. He's got a fuckin attitude that he thinks he's Mister It and he won't even give credit.' And this pitiful motherfucker has never asked me for any credit. But what he did was, he ran off at the mouth and let it get back to me. Now there might be two or three people in the bar doin some business with my product, and dudes will say, 'Is this Jimmy's? Oh wow, will you give me some?' Cause I have a reputation. I got good product, I don't bullshit, I'm not chintzy. And then this mouthy dude will show, and he's got cash, and he'll rap to me, 'Hey, you straight, man?' And I say I got nothin. And he sees my people doin business in the bar, and finally he will know I'm icing him and he will know why, when he thinks about it. All he had to do was shut up. I will never need this dude in my life, but if he wants the best that's available, he'll need me. So what he's gotta do now is get slick and have somebody else come to me and cop for him because he can't even come and cop no more. Or else he can go somewhere else and get seconds. But first is first and second is shit. Now he's hurt. And I'm just doin it to be nasty, cause it's not really necessary, except that you got to keep your thing together.

"See, these cats don't have any reason to dislike me, cause I never did anything to them. It's only a jealousy thing. But you better keep it to yourself, cause I get uptight if I hear it. All they know about me is I'm a nice guy, but I get superviolent. But then only when I'm provoked. Nobody can say Jimmy started somethin. But if you start it, you can bet your life that I'll finish it." He chuckled. "Don't fuck with Jim."

Suddenly he snapped his fingers and whirled back to the closet. He crouched down and reached in along the floor, and pulled out a small black holster with a thick, short strap. The holster held a snub-nosed .38 revolver. "I never showed you this," he said. "You know how you wear this?"

144

I thought for a moment. "It's a shoulder holster," I said. "It goes under the arm."

"Nope," he said with a sly smile. He bent over and strapped it above his ankle.

"But how can you wear that under the tight pants you wear?" I asked.

"Bells, man," he said, pulling his bell-bottom pants leg down over the holster. "Sometimes I wear bells. This comes in handy, cause like the takeoff man might know you carry a twenty-five in your pocket, but how many dudes would expect you to carry two heats?"

"But how can you get to it in a hurry?" I asked.

He started scratching his head and moving his legs as if in advanced agitation. "Like I'm nervous, right? Gettin taken off. I rap, 'Hey, man, listen now, you don't want to take me off, man, cause like . . .'"

He scratched here and there, and scratched his leg, and whoosh! the .38 was out. He had snapped up his leg and drawn.

I laughed. "Nobody's gonna let you start scratching your leg and messing around," I said.

He smiled. "You want to bet against me?"

"Hey Phyl! Phyl! Come here, quick!" Jimmy was sitting forward on the sofa, tapping the heels of his slippers on the floor, bouncing with urgency as he stared at a television commercial that featured a Jamaican with a large hat and extraordinary lips.

"Dig this jive," he said to me, laughing, "dig it, dig it, dig it! Hey Phyl!"

Phyl appeared. "What is it, Jim? What's the matter?"

"Turn it up, hurry, turn it up!"

Phyl sighed as she reached around the television and increased the volume. "Dag Jim," she said as she went away, "you called me all the way in here just for that?"

Jimmy was oblivious. "Dig that jive," he said to me, clapping his hands. "Wheeew! I wanted you to see that. Wow! Some of the shit they put down for *acting*. Man, I wish I was an actor."

He strolled to the center of the living room, smoothing his green robe as he went, then spreading his arms as if to present himself. "Shit, man, I could be good. I *know* I could be good. Cause a lot of what I do on the street is acting." He strode across his living-room proscenium, snapping his fingers, then stopped and whirled, holding his hands as if in preparation for a quick draw. "There's nothin to it. See, I got many ways of behaving. Like I got home manners and street manners. I can work my voice and whatnot. Now here I behave one way, you know, just rapping with you and normal and whatnot. I don't sound particularly black or anything, do I? I've even got jobs over the telephone, you know, 'Hello, I'm calling in response to your advertisement in *The New York Times*.' And then I show—shit, they get paranoid. But I don't sound particularly black. But on the street I'm like this. . . ."

He drew his shoulders back, narrowed his eyes, snapped his fingers once, and was instantly transformed into a majestic hustler. "I got a different voice, you know, 'Hey, what's happenin, baby?' I got a different look, like I'm icy all the time. There are cats that have never seen me smile. I got bitches come up to me and say, 'Damn, Jim, how come you so evil all the time?' I even got a walk— Hey Phyl? Come here a minute."

She walked in.

"Hey Phyl, tell him about my walk when you met me, you know, the one you didn't like."

"You always walked like you're walkin now."

"No, no, no, you know the way. Remember what you used to say?"

"Oh, you mean those little steps?"

146

"Yeah, that's it. Tell him about it."

Phyl smiled. "Yeah, well, it really bugged me, you know," she said to me, glancing up at him. "Jim used to take those little bitty steps. I thought it was effeminate. He still does it sometimes, when he's nervous."

"Yeah, or when I'm relaxing. That's my street walk, like this. . . ."

He walked across the room with mincing steps, snapping his fingers to each step, a very smooth, insolent gait that gave no bounce to his profile.

"You know what that's from?" he asked. "Dancing. Shit yeah. I used to be a dancer—Afro, Cuban, modern jazz, interpretive, ballet. That's why I have powerful legs. Hey Phyl, do I have legs like a girl? I have legs shaped like a girl's, right?"

"You mean nicely shaped legs?" Phyl said. "Yeah I guess so. I don't think they're like girls' legs, though."

"Yeah, but strong. I still walk like that sometimes. That's my street walk."

Having performed a show of ego so candid as to render it humble, Jimmy sat down. Phyl went back to whatever task she had left.

"Let me tell you something," Jimmy said. "Dancing is not feminine at all. To catch a broad weighing 130 pounds coming through the air, and look graceful—that is not feminine. A bullfighter's moves are superfeminine, but very strong, and actually very masculine. That's what prepared me for football, dancing."

He lowered his voice and leaned toward me. "Have you ever checked out the bods on some of those dancers? Hey! Phyl goes to dancing school now to keep her bod nice. I should do that too." He pulled open his robe and grabbed a handful of flesh above his waist. "You see all that? I *never* used to be like that. All this has come about in the past year, cause I can't run."

Phyl returned to the living room and plugged in the vacuum cleaner. Jocko, who had been chewing on a leather bone, scurried under the sofa. Jimmy pulled him back out. "Hey ol' badness, bark at the sweeper. That's what you *supposed* to do." He scratched the dog behind the ears with both hands and looked him in the eye. "Yeah, Jocko, you gonna win us some money."

"You really want him to win money?" I asked.

"Shit yeah," Jimmy said. Then he laughed. "Hey, we ain't no pimps, man. Everybody's gotta make their own way. Well, you know, I just want him to win the ribbons and the medals and the honor. I'm gonna take him to a good dog school. He's gonna be a good show dog. And if he didn't win anything, it would still be an experience, and a lot of fun, to put him in a dog show and see how he makes out." He put Jocko down and gave him a gentle prod in the rear with his slipper. "Hey, go eat your food, freshy. He eats biscuits and stuff, but he's got a sore throat. Vet said to give him cottage cheese."

But Jocko was sniffing instead at a dark spot he had just produced next to the sofa. Jimmy sighed, rubbed Jocko's nose in the spot, and then picked him up by the scruff of the neck and carried him into the bathroom.

"Don't carry him like that, Jimmy," Phyl said. "That's mean."

"That's how they carried him at the pet shop, baby," he answered, shutting the bathroom door. "It don't hurt him. Supposed to carry him that way."

"Aw, he's just a pup."

Jimmy chuckled.

"If you've never had a pet before," I said, "how do you know so much about your dog?"

He smiled and picked up a couple of books which were on top of the magazine rack. "Same way I get to know everything that I know," he said, handing me the two books

148

on care and feeding of Yorkshire terriers. "I *learn* it."

"Hey Jimmy?" Phyl called from a post outside the bathroom door. "He doesn't like to be in there."

"Let him be for a while. He's got to learn, baby."

"Aw . . ."

"Dog's got to be well-behaved," Jimmy said to me. "Just like children. I can't stand fresh children. Just be well-behaved. But on the other hand, I can't stand it when people treat a dog like a human. We were eating at Wells' once, you know that restaurant here in Harlem? We're in there eating chicken and waffles. And this black guy comes in with this white broad and she has a poodle. They order dinner, and a plate of food *for the dog on the floor.* Now on Park Avenue I see these women bring those nasty little dogs into the restaurants all the time. But it's against the law. They wouldn't let a black woman do that. I just don't think you should go into a restaurant and do like that. I really love my little dog, but I won't give him a plate to eat off that somebody else, or I, might have to eat off after him."

"You're getting fancy tastes," I said, "just *like* an actor."

Jimmy was pacing, pausing in front of the mirror, then pacing some more. "Hey man, I'm serious. I'd be a hell of an actor. It's conceit, I know, but I think I'd be good. I know I have a lot of heavy handicaps to overcome—things that I don't even talk about—but shit, if I couldn't be good, I wouldn't do it. I sure as hell wouldn't do it half-ass. I would study it, work at it. I would get training. Without one-hundred-percent effort you don't get nothing accomplished. I would sure as hell like to try."

"It would be interesting to see if you would freeze up in front of a camera," I said, recognizing that in his living room, his steely eyes and fluid movements could be impressive.

He stopped pacing and faced me, a sober, thoughtful expression in his face. "I think the street is a pretty good place to learn acting," he said. "You get a sense of little movements and looks that mean something. You learn what causes people to react certain ways. Like I don't have much education, but I know what makes people do and what makes people don't do. . . ."

"Hey Jimmy, can I let him out now?"

"Yeah, baby, go ahead."

Jimmy stared pensively into the mirror, then whirled back to me. "Hey listen. And the *scenes* I could do, you know from the street. Talk about realistic! I really know some scenes, man, the real shit, true events. Dig this: I almost got killed the other night."

He became quickly intense, his words were rapid. "I was in this bar, and I heard an explosion, a shot. I didn't know what was comin off, so I went for my gun. And whack! A sawed-off shotgun hits me across the wrist. 'Cool it,' this cat with the shotgun says. 'This is not your play.' And I didn't move, because that meant that nobody was after *me*. They had just shot this dude, and everybody just cooled it, because it didn't involve anybody. And then the owner says, 'What am I gonna do with this body in here?' And they say, 'Just cool it.' They take the body, clean up, back out, and it's over. Just like that. But had I come up with my gun . . ."

"Hey Jimmy, he won't come out. He's scared to come out of the bathroom."

Jimmy rolled his eyes toward the ceiling, and took a slow, deep breath.

14

Jimmy called at 1:30 A.M., his voice fervent from coke. "Hey man, listen. I'm gonna have to cancel our thing tomorrow. You remember that number I told you about?" (I groggily recalled that he had mentioned a pending sale of a quarter key at a price of $4,500.) "Well, it just came off, just now. Uh, not quite as big as I had planned. About thirty-one instead of forty-five. They didn't have the cash for the whole number. But I moved it. I really got to run now. Some cats would lay up and procrastinate after a number like that. But you got to move when your hand is hot. Back in a minute."

At the time, all it meant to me was another broken appointment. But the next day I got a different slant on the transaction from a third party.

"That was really something to watch," the man said. "What happened was that Jimmy's quality was just not up to what he promised, and he was dealing with somebody who was just as smart as he was, dealer to dealer. See, this guy's lines had dried up temporarily, and he needed some top coke in a hurry to keep his own customers happy. So I put him on to Jimmy, and of course Jimmy said he could produce it. But when Jimmy showed with his product, the man tasted it and said it wasn't as good as he needed. So Jimmy had to take off and come back later with some better stuff. And even then, the guy decided it wasn't good enough to go the whole way, to two-eighths. But it was good enough for him to take some of it—about thirty-one hundred dollars, that sounds about right.

"But what an education, watching those two sharp dealers going at each other. You know, they'd taste and rap and discuss. Jimmy would admit that the other cat's stuff was good, but of course he wouldn't go so far as to admit that his own didn't match it. I got a feeling maybe those two can get together and do a thing together, you know, pool their resources. Might give Jimmy the financial flexibility he needs."

"Tired, man, that's how I am," Jimmy said. "Leggin it all the time."

The phone chimed, and he let it chime twice before he picked it up. "Yeah," he said, his voice raspy with sleep. "Okay, in an hour. Bet that." He put the phone down and leaned back, rubbing his eyes. "Tired all the time."

"I understand you had quite a session the other night," I said, "trying to come off with that quarter-key."

A flicker of suspicion darted in his eyes as he glanced at me before snorting a two-and-two.

"Tell me," I said, "supposing *I* had a friend who wanted to buy a quarter-key, forty-five hundred dollars' worth of coke, but the guy wanted to sit down directly with you. What would you say to that?"

Jimmy sniffed a couple of times as he folded up the aluminum foil and put it on the table. "Cordin to who you are. If you're a person I could really really trust and you knew the other cat very well, very well—then if you were a very good friend I would probably say, bet to that. But usually it's like, I have some people that I know who know what I do, and they might cut into somebody that wants something. Like you have a friend who wants good coke. And you don't have any coke, but you have access to good coke from me. Either you're a go-between or you'd cut me into your friend. Usually you're a go-between. And we set up a deal. I usually don't want to meet the buyer. I don't want to know anybody, not until I *know* them—you dig what I'm saying. Okay, we set up a deal and I give you a sample to take to the buyer. The sample is according to how much you're gonna sell. So here I'm gonna sell a quarter-key for forty-five hundred, and I'd give you a quarter, a tablespoon, as a sample. That's worth about $150. Now the sample represents what you're gonna get so long as you don't fuck with me. You can't cheat on the sample. Risky. Get you shot."

"Then if you *did* sit down directly with the prospective buyer," I said, "would you haggle over price?"

"We wouldn't haggle. Well, he might want to haggle a little bit, you know, get me down five hundred, maybe a grand if he thought he could. Okay, say he wants to pay four thousand. I want forty-five hundred for a quarter-key. So what I might do is take a little of the quality out, and put a little cut in, and give him a quarter of a key. I'm not fucking him around, and it's not necessary to tell him what I'm doing. I'm telling him my price for a quarter-key of the quality he sampled is forty-five hundred. He says four thousand. Four thousand? Okay, bet to that. Give me the four thousand and I'll get back to you in fifteen minutes or a half-hour. And I come back with a quarter of a key. You get what you pay for, and I'm gettin my price. Listen to this: He buys a quarter of a key, and I tell him I'm gonna guarantee it on a 2½ to a three. Hear what I'm saying? A 2½ to a three. Now, he wants it at a cheaper price, so which level of cut is it going to be closer to?"

"Supposing he's tough," I said, "and he says don't mess with me, I want it guaranteed on a three."

"He doesn't speak to me that way," Jimmy said brusquely, "not if he's buying a *key,* not if he's buying *five* keys. If he's buying my product he doesn't speak to me that way, because I don't allow it. Go somewhere else and buy it. I don't need your business. I'd turn away a motherfucker with a million dollars if he got nasty. I'd tell him to kiss my ass. Because the market is going to be there. I don't need his money. I'm not that hungry. Cause dig this: I'll take that same quarter of a key and put it into eighths, for twenty-two, twenty-three hundred apiece, right? I'm gonna make my money anyway."

"But you would prefer to sell a quarter-key than two separate eighths, right?"

"I'm not gonna kiss anybody's ass to do it. I'm not gonna let him fuck with my product. He can't tell me how to do my thing. I set up a price in my mind what I'm gonna sell it for. And I'm not going below that price, no matter what. It's not worth it. I'm not gonna be handling coke just to be handling it. And if I don't make enough money so that I feel it's advantageous to do it, fuck you, I won't sell it to you. Listen: Which is easier to do, buy good coke or sell good coke? Much easier to sell it."

"But one time you told me that the man above you was dependent on you because coming off with large quantities of drugs was not easy."

"Hey, nothin in this business is easy. But you don't make it easier for yourself by letting people fuck you around. You think it's easy to find a reliable man to deal you a weight of coke? You think that's easy? I'm in the business, and say I have three connections. One goes out of business and two get killed, which is real. I'm out of business myself. Then I got to look around for somebody else, and in doing that I'm gonna get beat, gonna get burned, gonna buy garbage. So when you find somebody that's reliable and good, man, you stick to them. You meet their price. There are fairly stand-ard prices. You don't haggle and fuck around. Cats you deal with have been checked out. Cat comes to me, he knows that he'll get what he's paying for, and he'll be satisfied, and he can come back. There's not that many people out there you can go up to and get a quarter-key or a half-key. What the big buyer is looking for is quality. If the quality is there, you'll get your money."

"How can you be sure about quality?" I asked.

"Very first thing you do is check your quality out. I do that myself. I don't need anybody else. I know enough about what I'm buying. You can tell the difference."

He took the aluminum-foil packet from the table beside him and opened it on the sofa. "Okay, look here. See those rocks, like Boulder Dam? Those big pieces here and here? You got rocks in there like that, that's one mark of quality. Rocks are pure. Can't crush the rocks with your fingers. You leave a few of them in there to show the quality. Here, wet your finger and taste this. . . . Now, that is on a one, cut once. All right." He reached into his robe pocket and took out another small dollar-bill packet and opened it. "Now this. . . . That's more bitter, right? That's on a half. If you taste some that's more bitter, you know it's better. That's another test. And then of course you can snort a one and know immediately. You get to know your shit."

"Why the dollar bill?" I asked. "Is that just for show?"

"Naw. The thing is that aluminum foil, when you open it a few times, it begins to crack and leak. Good paper is better. And the paper they make money out of is about the best you can get, lasts the longest. That's all."

"Don't you have to trust somebody when you're buying?"

"I don't trust shit. I've got to be shown. It's got to pass all my tests, then I'll buy it. You can't sell nobody drugs by running off at the mouth. Drugs sell themselves. You don't have to take nobody's word for it. All you got to do is know what you're doin, and then you know what you're gettin."

"Supposing you had a key of pure coke," I said, "and I wanted an eighth. How much would you cut it?"

"Depending upon the quality. Let's assume that the

quality I got was a three. I'd probably give it to you guaranteed on a two. That means I would take half an eighth and put it on a one, making it into an eighth. That leaves you room for two cuts. Now, that would cost you probably twenty-three hundred. You'd probably put at least a one, maybe a one and a half on it, and sell half-quarters and quarters."

"Supposing I don't want to mess with cutting it. I just want to retail it, be a middleman. Why wouldn't you just put it in shape for me to sell as is?"

Jimmy sighed. "God bless the child that's got his own. You leave it to me to do, and I might put it on a *four* and give it to you. I might fuck you around, cause when you say to do it all, I know you don't know what you're doin."

"But if I'm a friend and I just want to be an outlet . . ."

"No, no, that's not real. Cause, say you want to sell a half-quarter, seventy-five dollars' worth of coke. Now if you're gonna do that, you want a certain quality, cut a certain amount. You got an eighth, and you already had me cut it to sell in half-quarters. Now here comes a man to you and wants to buy a piece—six hundred dollars' worth of coke. You have to give him better quality. But now if you've already had your coke cut to sell in half-quarters, well how you gonna take the cut back out of it to make the quality better so you can sell a piece? You cut it as you sell it."

"Okay," I said, "suppose I don't want to get into the business at all. But maybe I have some rich friends that want some coke. I just want to provide them with coke. Why would I want to bother cutting it?"

"Cause then you know what you're doing. See, otherwise you've taken my word for what I'm doing. That's only halfway good. Unless you really, really, really know the people, man, you can get beat to death doin that kind of shit. There's a difference between buying dope and buying scrambled eggs, you know."

I sat absorbing his hard-nosed reckoning, so inextricably woven with vanity and bluff as to keep—I could imagine—both student and customer off balance. "Okay," I said, "then if I know what I'm doing, why don't I come to you and say I want an eighth of pure coke?"

"Cause I don't want to sell you an eighth of pure. You don't sell an eighth pure. Oh, you can, of course, and then you pay a lot more. If you buy an eighth, you really can't look for more than a two. That's decent. To buy a quarter-key and get a 2½, that's respectable. To get it better than that, you go into the realm of being unreal. If you're buying an eighth of pure, I would have to tell you give me three thousand dollars. And you would probably say fuck that. Sure, there's cats that come to me and say give me two hundred dollars' worth of pure coke. It would be about, well, say two-fifty of pure coke would be less than a tablespoonful, less than a quarter. You could make it into three tablespoons at least, sell them for one-fifty each. But I don't sell it that way unless it's a friend. Then he's buying it to sniff, so he will put a one on it and snort it up."

"But if it's a friend of yours, you, the expert, might just as well put the cut in for him, right?"

"Listen: Anybody spending that kind of money for coke knows what he's doing. Would you go out and spend two, three hundred dollars on something you didn't know anything about? Neither would anybody else. Three hundred dollars is a lot of money to spend on blow. You say you would if you had the money. Shit, if I had the cash I'd buy a jet plane, but you're talking about having so much money you don't give a damn where it goes. Some people go out and buy a fifty-nine-cent bottle of wine. That's their drink. Maybe you go out and buy some good Scotch that's very expensive. There's *your* drink. You spend the extra money because you like it and you know something about the quality of what you're buying."

157

"By the time the man on the street gets a snort of coke," I said, "how many times has the price been marked up?"

"The price hasn't really gone up. The quality has come down. My supplier, I'd say he probably cops and puts it on a half to a one. He's making from fifty to one hundred percent profit. And I'm making the same, and the cat I sell to is making the same. Let's say my supplier has a piece of coke, cost him six hundred, on a three. He puts a half on it, making it into a piece and a half, with room for 2½ more cuts. Now if he sells me a piece, he will charge me the same thing he paid for it, but it's been cut a half a time. And he keeps a half a piece for himself. Now, I take the piece, and I usually put a one on it, right? That means I have two pieces now, on a 1½. I can't sell them for top dollar any more, since they are only on a 1½, so I sell the pieces for $550 each. Now, a cat buys a piece from me for $550 with a 1½ on it, right? He puts another one on it. Then he sells $20 spoons, $40 spoons, half-quarters for $65–$75. Now that coke has been cut 2½ times. So this last man can guarantee it on a half, meaning it can still take another half-cut, because it was coke that could stand a three, and that is what commercial coke that you buy on the street is usually cut."

Jimmy yawned and stretched, and then looked at me out of the corner of his eye. "Hey," he said, smiling, "you lookin to get into the business or something?"

"I'm just working," I said.

"Heh-heh, yeah."

"You gonna be in the business much longer?" I asked.

"The way I'm doing it now? Not much longer at all. Very short-lived what I'm doing now, cause it's getting better all the time. And as it gets better and better and better, there comes a time when I delegate more things to people. I'll tell you what's going to happen. I'm going to get myself a backer."

"That's what you've been saying."

He laughed. "It's out there. There are people talking about investing in my thing." He leaned toward me in confidential mode. "Tell me something. You give me a thousand dollars, and I'll show you what happens. Double your money in no time."

I was stuck for a reply, and he laughed at that too.

15

Jimmy sat on the sofa dressed in an orange silk undershirt and a flowered towel, his supper tray across his lap, watching a television program called *The Immortal* about a man whose blood had eternal restorative powers. Phyl, her long black hair over her shoulders, wearing tight slacks and Scandinavian clogs, sat on the floor with her arms around her knees. Slick sat on a chair on the opposite side of the room, his applejack cap tilted forward. He rubbed his leather sneakers together occasionally. His pistol lay on a table to one side. His girl, Fifi, dressed in slacks, sat on the sofa next to Jimmy. Every few seconds Jocko would zip soundlessly across the room to retrieve his leather bone and drop it at the feet of whoever threw it last time.

The program concerned an old man who was dying, and who was holding the Immortal prisoner for handy transfusions. But the Immortal escaped, and for the duration he was hunted by the old man's goons. Everyone in the room watched attentively.

In a crucial lapse, the Immortal forgot his gun. Jimmy slapped his thigh. "Will you look at that dude," he said, pointing at the TV. "First thing the dumb dude does is lose his roscoe. Shit, that's not real." Slick shook his head.

And when Mrs. Immortal, over the telephone, begged her hiding husband to permit her to rejoin him, Jimmy seemed genuinely annoyed. "She *loves* him. Wow. And what's she gonna do? Lead the old man's dudes right to her man, put him in a trap. He ought to smack that bitch."

He was right about the trap, of course. There was yet another chase, with the Immortal in a Shelby Mustang pursued by the goons in a ponderous Chrysler. "No dudes gonna catch that Shelby, huh, Slick?"

"No sir, man, fuckin Chrysler," Slick said.

Finally the Chrysler was left nose down in a river. Jimmy bounced up off the sofa and laughed. "Shit, man, couldn't catch that Shelby unless you had a half-ass flunky dude at the wheel of it. That'll move, that car."

"What's a Shelby?" Fifi asked.

"Shit, they use that for racing," Jimmy said. "But dig this, I got 472 under the hood of my hog. And the seventy-one's got 500. That's what I want. Now I tell you, let anybody try and catch me goin across the Bronx. Let em try. Cause my hog will *move.*"

The program concluded, Jimmy bent down and scooped up little Jocko, holding him behind the forelegs, face to face. "You wittow devow, wittow, wittow, devow. What'sa matter with yo bad sewf?" He turned to me. "We bought him a bed, you know, one of those wicker things with a roof. But he can't get through the hole, you know, can't quite get up into the hole yet."

It was eleven P.M. and the men were a couple of hours late getting out on the street. Jimmy stretched and started out of the room to dress.

"Do you think that could really happen?" Fifi asked.

"What?" Slick replied.

"A guy with that kind of blood."

"Shiiit," Jimmy said, stopping in the doorway.

"Don't say 'shit' when you don't know," Slick said.

Jimmy came back in. "What do you mean, don't know?"

"Lot of things you don't know, don't nobody know," Slick said.

"Like what?" Jimmy said.

"Like what causes things."

"Like what causes *what?*"

"Like what causes everything, you know, rain, and things to grow, and things to happen and shit."

"God causes it, right?" Phyl said.

"Yeah," Fifi said.

"It's the universal mind of man," Slick announced, straightening his back and putting his hands on his knees.

"The *what?*" Jimmy said.

"The universal mind of man. You know, it's what's inside of man that causes things to happen. It's something inside of everything."

"Like what?" Jimmy asked disdainfully.

"Like—well, listen: When they landed on the moon, when men landed on the moon for the first time, why do you suppose it rained for three solid days?"

"Why?" Jimmy said, cocking his head and putting his fists on his hips.

"Because the universal mind of man was *apprehensive,* you know, people all over worried and shit, worried about what was going on, worried about the men. And inside themselves, that worry . . ."

"Caused it to rain for three days? Shiiit," Jimmy said, chuckling as he stomped out of the room.

"Damn, Jimmy," Slick called plaintively after him, "there you go, lookin down your nose at what I'm sayin, raising your voice, you know, shoutin me down instead of listening."

Jimmy stalked back into the room, flashing a cocky smile, glancing at me. "I ain't shoutin you down. But what are you sayin? I mean, what is this shit about rain for three days?"

"Well, didn't it rain for three days, three solid days, while they were landin on the moon?"

"I don't know what the fuck it did. But whatever it did, it didn't do it everywhere. It could rain for three days in Harlem and not mean shit."

162

"Now listen to me, Jim," Slick said with a trace of whine. "Just listen now. It rained for three days, three solid days. And people were worried about the men on the moon, right? You got to admit that. And I'm sayin it's not just that one isolated thing. The universal mind of man causes things to happen. I mean it's a *force*. Like some people might call it God."

Jimmy was tightening the belt on a pair of tight maroon pants. "Now you're talkin about me," he said, smirking.

"What?" Slick said.

"You mentioned God," Jimmy said, flashing a narrow-eyed smile at me. "You must mean me, cause that's what you said. And here I am." He spread his arms as proof.

"Now see, Jim, there you go," Slick said, wagging his head. "That's the way you treat people, you know, puttin 'em down, bein so quick, puttin down their *minds*."

"I ain't puttin down nothin. I'm just askin questions. Like, why did it just rain in Harlem if everybody was worried about the moon?"

"How do you know it just rained in Harlem?"

"Well it sure as hell didn't rain everyplace, because that sure would have been an *event*."

"I'm just saying that things that happen are caused by a kind of force inside things. Like, dig this: What causes a blade of grass to grow?"

Jimmy snorted. "The universal fuckin mind of man," he said, turning to the full-length mirror on the closet door.

"That's right! Now that's right, whether you laugh or not. Somethin in that blade of grass wants to grow, so it grows."

Jimmy tucked his .25 into a side pocket in his trousers and turned to face Slick, still smiling. He spread his fingers and drew up his hands slowly in front of him, seeming to be carefully forming a blade of grass and making it grow. "You mean that, like here's this blade of grass, right? And it ain't growin or nothin. It ain't doin shit. And then one day that blade of grass says, 'I feel like growin,' and so it grows?"

163

"That's exactly right."

"Now," Jimmy continued, "supposing there's no rain. Will it still grow?"

"It will want rain, and so it will rain."

Jimmy shook his head as if to clear it from a blow and laughed. "Well, what the fuck happens if the rain don't want to rain? I mean, maybe the rain is sittin up there sayin, 'I don't want to rain on that grass.' How does the universal mind in the blade of grass get to the universal mind in that rain and tell it what to do?"

"Doesn't God make the grass grow?" Phyl asked.

"It don't matter whether you call it God or not," Slick said in gentler tones to Phyl. "The important thing is that something inside the grass makes it want to grow. It's the universal mind of man, a universal intelligence. It's a spiritual thing, whatever you call it. But it's inside everything."

"Do you realize," Jimmy said, chopping the air with his hand, "that you're not really saying anything? Not anything at all. Because all you're saying is that things happen because they happen. The grass grows because the grass grows —that's saying the same thing. It just happens that grass, being grass, grows."

"Now you're just twisting my words," Slick said. "Look, do you recall that life began in the sea? Do you recall that the first life were fishes, and then they became birds? Why do you suppose they became birds?"

"Why?"

"Because the fish wanted to fly, that's why. Some fish just wanted to fly so bad, and the universal mind in the fish made it develop wings so that it could fly. The fish took wing because he *wanted* to fly."

"Oh man," said Jimmy, wincing.

"Yeah, dig it, dig it, dig it," Slick said, leaning forward on his chair and stabbing the air with his index finger. "Now do you know that the horse at one time was no bigger than Jocko there?"

164

"The what?"

"The horse, man. It was at one time in history no bigger than a little dog. And the horse must have said something like, 'Hey shit, I want to be bigger.' And in time it got bigger, because it wanted to."

"Slick, that is so much bullshit," Jimmy said loudly.

"Now there you go, just trying to overwhelm me with your voice," Slick said.

"That's just what he does," Phyl added as she curled up and began combing Jocko's hair. "He starts talking so loud."

"Okay, okay," Jimmy said, his eyes flitting from Phyl to me to Slick. "I want to fly. I want to fly so bad. Why the hell can't I fly?"

"You *can*," Slick said, satisfaction in his voice for the first time. "Man, with his intelligence, built the airplane, a machine to fly even better than a bird."

"Why didn't we just grow wings?"

"Because that was too crude a method for something of man's superior intelligence. Dig the fact that no bird, not the fastest bird, can fly as fast as the slowest airplane."

Jocko started coughing, a miniature wheeze that shook his body. "He's been doing that for a week," Phyl said. "We have to take him to the vet tomorrow. Last time he gave us some cough medicine for him, but he's still coughing."

Jimmy used the respite to duck out for more of his wardrobe.

"You know, Phyl," Fifi said in a questioning voice, "Slick really believes that when I was bleeding last week it was because I *wanted* to, this same kind of thing. I wanted to *bleed*."

"That's right," Slick said, nodding. "It was induced by her mind. That's so. She went to the hospital, and they told her there was nothing wrong."

"Yeah, but then when I went home it started again," Fifi said, still looking at Phyl.

165

"Because you wanted it to," Slick persisted.

"No, that's not true. Listen, Phyl. I was in my room, and Slick was angry about something, and he wouldn't come in and sleep with me. But I wanted a little romance, and so I said, 'Slick, come on in here.' And he came in and laid down beside me and shooosh, it just started just like that."

"You're just proving my point," Slick said, without rancor. He leaned forward toward Phyl. "Look, Phyl, it's true. Once you have selected your goal, things are bound to happen. It's like when you take a bust, you know, it was bound to happen, it was meant to be. When you set out on a certain path, then certain things must happen. So like a bust is just something that has to happen on your way to your goal."

Phyl knitted her brows as she pondered that. Jimmy came back in, wearing a black leather vest with his maroon trousers. "You don't even know if you're gonna be alive tomorrow, Slick," he said.

Slick ignored the comment. He clasped his hands together and looked intently at Phyl and said softly, "Phyl, how come you are a girl, a black girl, right now?"

She shrugged. "What do you mean? Because my parents were black and because I was born."

"The universal mind of man. Because your father and your mother got together, and your father wanted you to be made, and he wanted that sperm to get there, and he knew that sperm was going to get there, and he knew that you would be made."

Jimmy gave a deep, throaty chuckle. "Shit, her father wasn't thinking about no sperm goin nowhere." He swung around and slapped my palms as he laughed.

"You don't know so much about it, Jim," Slick said, pouting a little. "Hey listen. Things *mean* things. Let me ask you something: When somebody dies, he always breathes out—whooo—breathes out, right? When some-

166

body dies he always breathes out. You know what that is? That's the spirit leavin, the universal mind of that man is leavin."

"Well, I can tell you somethin, Slick," Jimmy said, facing the mirror again. "I've seen people die breathin out, and I've seen people die breathin in, and I've seen people die not breathin at all."

"Damn, Jim," Slick said. "You got to believe *somethin*. God ain't just a dude. People believe. There's such a thing as premonitions, people believing things that later happen."

Jimmy started out of the room again. Over his shoulder he said, "Yeah, I had a premonition."

"What?" Slick said.

"I had a premonition a few weeks ago." He paused and absorbed the interests of the room focused on him. "I had a premonition Richard was a cop." He smiled wryly and exited.

"Aw, Jim," Phyl said.

Slick exhaled in a subdued hiss. He looked at his sneakers. Jocko coughed. Slick took an aluminum-foil pouch from his pocket, opened it, and with the extra-long nail of his little finger scooped up some coke and snorted it. He passed it to Fifi, who did the same.

As Phyl continued combing Jocko's hair, she said thoughtfully, "You know, I have a friend who when she gets high says she can see molecules, you know, real molecules, individual molecules in things."

Slick nodded. "I can understand that. I can see where that would be possible."

Jimmy was back, smiling devilishly at himself in the mirror and patting his Afro. "What did they look like?" he said.

"What do you mean, what did they look like?" Phyl asked.

"Well, if she saw molecules, she must know what they

look like. What did they look like?"

"Dag, Jim, I don't know."

Jimmy chuckled. The phone chimed, and he answered it. He mumbled some mm-hms, and something about an "eighth," and then hung up and went cheerfully over to slap Slick's palms. "Hey, you know who that was? You know who? Yeah. Comin off with an eighth tonight. Hey, an *eighth,* man." And they skinned again.

The television was still on, and suddenly the attention of the room was caught by some film of a raid on a Black Panther headquarters in New Orleans. Faces in the room hardened a little. "Fuckin bulls," Jimmy muttered. "And they wonder why things happen."

That led around to the subject of Muhammad Ali, who was about to fight for the first time after being barred from the boxing ring for three years because of his refusal to be drafted into the Army. He was going to fight Jerry Quarry, the Irishman.

"He just may croak Quarry," Jimmy said, "because can you imagine how he has stored up three years of hate?"

I mentioned that Ali's recent statements didn't sound cocky.

"Well," Jimmy said, "it's just like when the man has his head in the lion's mouth. He tickles his chin, but he doesn't try to kick his ass. But there will be an ass-kicking in that ring, right, Slick?"

"Dig it!"

Ali's claim to draft exemption was, of course, on religious grounds, that he was a Black Muslim. That led to discussion of the Muslims and the late Malcolm X.

"Malcolm was just hustling by all that religion just like everybody else until he split with Elijah Muhammad," Jimmy argued. "He began trying to do good after that, but it was just plain hustling before."

Phyl disagreed. "I think Malcolm got his message to help

people when he was in prison," she said, "just like it says in his book."

Jimmy scoffed. "He would have got it anyway, cause the message was you can't go on hustling people forever."

Jimmy and Slick threw their reverence behind the late Martin Luther King. "Yeah," Slick said, "all those people that down him today forget that it was King who was so cool all those years up before the rednecks when there wasn't no big publicity and support."

"Yeah, King was—hey!" Jimmy said. "You talk about guts, you got to talk about Martin Luther King. You know how much guts it must take to stand up before a whole bunch of rednecks with guns and shit, motherfuckers who hate your black ass clear through, and tell them you may kill me, you may hurt me, we ain't got no guns, but we're movin anyway. Hey! And I think he played it straight, clear through, all his life."

I was interested in pursuing this appraisal of the hustlers, but Phyl stepped in.

"Okay, you guys, come on, get going," she said in the manner of a wife shooing her husband off to work. "You're already late."

"You *want* them to go?" I asked.

"Well, the quicker they leave, the quicker they're back," she said. "It's tough enough getting Jimmy up in the morning anyway. You know, he'll answer the phone, like when you call, right? And he'll talk to you, but he won't even be awake. Isn't that right, Jim?"

"Yeah, it can happen. Although if you're talking to me you'll think I'm awake."

"But he won't remember it later," Phyl said.

"They both want us to make sure we get them up in the morning," Fifi said, "and then they yell at us for doing it."

"That's true," Phyl said, putting her hand on Jimmy's shoulder. "And you know what he likes me to do in the morning?" Jimmy winced. "He likes me to wipe his face with a warm rag, isn't that right, Jim?"

"Mmm," he said without expression. "Time to go."

Jimmy's outfit was complete now, maroon trousers, black alligator shoes, black sweater with a leather vest, white applejack cap. He carried a heavy swagger stick with a demon's-head figure on the end. He stood before the mirror and went over the outfit carefully, touching here and there, tapping the butt of his gun, the sides of his Afro, the gold bracelet with diamonds studded to spell "Jimmy."

Slick tucked his pistol into his trouser pocket, patted Jocko on the head, and they walked toward the door.

"In the morning," Jimmy said to Phyl.

"Bye," she said cheerfully as she locked the door behind us. We rode down the elevator in silence. When the door opened at the lobby we were confronted by a large German shepherd with a small master. Slick stiffened for an instant, then we stepped out and passed by.

"I want me a dog like that," he said as we pushed open the lobby door and felt the cool night air, "only bigger. So I can train him to collect money, so he can smell it. And when the dude says, 'Hey man, I haven't got it,' the dog will start sniffing and come right up with it."

We parted, and Jimmy and Slick walked off into the Harlem dark to sell their eighth.

As I sit watching on television the nation's third landing of men on the moon, I ponder the notion of a "universal mind of man" and its relationship to Jimmy. For all his sassy disdain for such dreams, he is himself no prisoner of reality, that smug doctrine of prissiest truth. What is cause and effect in the matter of things that come to pass? Who dares predict the yield of a relentless confidence? When a dream succeeds, is it due to its confluence with simple fate, or to the brave, tenacious faith of the dreamer? Jimmy would not call himself a dreamer, nor his goals dreams; yet he is, they are, if a dream may be defined as all that has not yet been shown to be. And without honoring his dreams or means, it is his regal certitude, I think, one comes to respect, if not always to like. It is also a characteristic good for business, if you are a hustler.

"Yeah, I can dig that," said a mutual friend. "I didn't used to like him too much. But in time I came to be—what is it?—*charmed* by the audacious bastard. I got so mad at him the other day I was gonna whip his ass. I mean it. I told him to leave all his armor at home and I'd meet him in an alley or anywhere. We just dropped it. You know, shit, I *like* the motherfucker."

He is a big, strong man, this friend, educated, militantly black, involved in a legitimate business. But like so much of licit Harlem, he lives on the edge of the hustling world. Once when I stopped up to see him his right hand was badly swollen. He had been hounded for weeks by a fanatical black nationalist who incessantly challenged his blackness, until my friend could take no more. "I have paid my motherfuckin dues," my friend said angrily, "and I am just as black as any motherfucker on the street corner with a bullhorn. And I finally just had to deck the crazy bastard." So now, for a few days, he would carry a pistol, "because you never know where these cats' heads are."

Not long ago, a young black actress, a beautiful, talented, forceful Harlem native, whose dues, too, have been paid, was nearly in tears because she had seen on a bus a young black boy snatch a purse from an old black lady, and get away with it. And then minutes later she was walking down a main Harlem street when a sidewalk hawker said, "Hey baby, you're so beautiful I'd like to eat your pussy." She responded with tough words, and the hawker was ashamed. She saved sad words for later when she could take a snort of coke and talk it out.

I know a fellow who was once part of a famous song-and-

171

dance team. After performing in Harlem for several years, he traveled all around the world, and was in some Hollywood movies. Now he lives in Harlem again, and drives a limousine-for-hire, and worries about the street. "You can look out this window," he told me one day, "and watch the taxicabs. And watch the kids standing around. They're watching the taxicabs, and when the right one stops, they'll grab open the door and snatch the money and beat it. That's not the Harlem I knew, man."

One night I stopped by to say hello to a young black businessman who was working late. He was staring out the window. "I sit up here workin my ass off day after day," he said, "and still I don't have anything, really. I'm not complaining, you know, I'm not starving, but you look around out there and see where the money is, and I sometimes wonder, if I were doing it over, would I go all through college and all that shit and come back here and sit in an office and deal with all the racists and all, for what I get out of it. I wonder if I wouldn't be out there on the street." He turned to me and laughed. "What I mean is, some days you want to say, 'Fuck it.' "

I am wary of Harlem vignettes, because writing them is simple, like going South to write about bigots. But if one is to record the confessions of dreamers, one must try to sense the circumstances.

I asked my friend, "What does Jimmy really make?"

"Oh, I think at this point Jimmy probably averages profit of five to eight hundred dollars a week. So in white-collar terms, we're probably talking about a salary of something like thirty thousand a year. Sure, it's tax-free, but you take a bust or something, it probably comes down to the same, or less. In any case, it's still three or four times better than he would ever have made it nine-to-five. The life style is deceptive. You know, you can get an Eldorado up here for between thirty-five hundred and six thousand. The tele-

172

visions and everything are bought hot, maybe a third of what it costs you. And then the clothes, he has 'loft privileges'—he can buy from warehouses—because he buys volume, maybe once a year, like many athletes. So he may go down one day and buy two, three hundred dollars' worth of sweaters, you know. And after all that, of course, he can get shot."

"What about the hundred-thousand-dollar goal?" I asked.

"Oh, I think that's just a figure that rolls off the tongue easily. He'd probably pull back if he had fifty thousand, or thirty thousand, or maybe even twenty thousand laid aside."

There he was, lying naked on his belly, bending up backwards, smiling crookedly, his elbows not quite straight under the strain, his head nearly bald, round and soft all over: the Dealer at three months.

"I was the same age in that picture as Jocko was when we bought him," Jimmy said.

We were holding the scrapbook between us, on our knees. Pictures of dress occasions, guests, family, football players, the earlier Jimmy with hair more curly than Afro and combed and parted, B.J. posed aggressively in his karate robe, Jimmy in his; Jimmy's baby girl a year or so before she died.

"Some of that shit seems so long ago," Jimmy said, flipping slowly through the pages.

Phyl came in with some snapshots of her recent vacation. Jimmy went through them rapidly. "None of you in a bathing suit?"

"Naw."

"Why not?"

"Aw Jim, I don't know. We just didn't get around to it. Do you guys want to eat?"

"Yeah, in a little while, doll, just call us when it's ready."

Jocko trotted in, his furry legs in blurred motion. "Hey,

let me show you what Jocko can do. Hey Jocko, come here." Jimmy snapped his fingers above the sofa cushions. "Come on, up, up, up." Jocko leaped mightily toward the sofa seat, but fell short and bounced off the front. "He can do it. He just learned, or just got big enough. Come on, Jocko." Jocko leaped again, got a toehold, and scrambled aboard the sofa. Jimmy grinned. "That's quite a leap for a dog that size, huh?"

He took Jocko in his lap. "We've had him on the street, you know, but the dude . . ." Jimmy began to laugh. "Hey, you know he won't walk? He doesn't dig the noise and all the people and cars and stuff. So you got to carry him. Ol' badness."

He put Jocko down.

"You know, when you met me, I was nine thousand dollars in debt, had no product. Now I have five thousand worth of product—what I have paid for it—and about two, three thousand in my pocket, and I don't owe a dime."

"When I met you," I said, "you talked as if you were *already* flying."

We both smiled.

"Yeah," he said. "But there were really some shaky times. Like, on the street in those early days, that's when I *really* had to fight to prove myself, you know. I mean *really*. Hey Phyl?"

Phyl was walking past the door, and Jimmy stopped her. "Remember then how I used to come home with bruised knuckles, swollen hands and shit?"

Phyl nodded. "He was always saying he got taken off or something."

"Hey, baby, it was real! Cause dig it: You get a new cat in the bar. Five or six cats in the corner watching him. 'Who's that dude? Who does he work for? He's an independent. Oh yeah?' And then one of them comes over to you and says, 'I understand you got some good coke. Give it to me.' Hey, heh-heh. Right then you got to prove yourself. And there were fights. Then when I came out of the hospital, you know, from my ankle thing, I was a nasty, bitter motherfucker and I was ready to fight *anybody* over *anything*."

"That's true," Phyl said. "He was so ornery, always wanting to punch somebody."

"Yeah. Hey!" He tapped her arm. "You remember that time I hit the dude with my crutch? Hooo, man. My first day back in the bar this motherfucker comes over and says, 'Well, what you gonna do now that you're a cripple?' Oooh, man, I dropped those crutches and went after that dude, busted him up good. Also busted a couple stitches. And the pain the next day—whew!—it was a *smoker*."

He leaned back and stared at the ceiling. "But I just always believed my hustle thing was going to go. Even when I was a nine-to-fiver, you know, I was arrogant. *Something* was going to go. And now it's going. And there'll come a time when I'm really retired—that is to say, inactive. But I'll get to a point where I don't really do anything except sit back like, well, like being a general when there's a war going on. You know, they have generals that haven't fired a gun in twenty years. They sit back, and to them it's a master game of chess. I probably will always have my fingers into something, making money my way because it's fast money. Unless I become a millionaire, or get to a point where I'm really independently wealthy and I don't have to. Then I wouldn't any longer. But until that time I will. But I just personally will get farther and farther away from it to the point where it's harder to touch me. But there's always something to be made money on quick in the street. Doesn't have to be drugs. Here's a cat, say, has a truckload of hot color TV's. Here's a cat has a truckload of mink coats. It's not risky. You don't have to touch 'em. Get one of your lieutenants, have him buy the truckload. Then have him put

175

a couple of cats to work sellin 'em, make your profit. Where's the risk? It's not as risky as dope, because dope you can really be cheated on, so you really have to be able to trust the cat to let him handle your dope, or your coke, or your reefer, or whatever. But that's why the money is so fast, because of the risk. There's no risk in taking a nine-to-five. It's consistent, and it's within the law, and the money is slow as hell."

"Then I guess you don't envy the man in an office," I said, "drawing a large, safe salary, and able to count on it."

"Naw. More power to him. What? Me sit behind a desk all day? People only do that because they can't do anything else. His shit is consistent and it's geared to be stretched out over a period of time, maybe increase a little bit each year. It's a guarantee, more or less. Whereas when you do your own thing there are no guarantees, but if you *do* it, tseeeooo! You can become a millionaire overnight."

"But you're still talking about hustling," I said. "I thought you were going to get out."

"Okay, sure. I'd like to open some legitimate business. Big liquor store in the right location, because people that don't have money to go out and eat in a restaurant have money to go and buy booze for the weekend. A bar is fabulous in the right location. But you know what my dream is? I'd like to open a black Playboy Club. Have you heard of a black club that had very good food, very good entertainment, and where you could dance, in Harlem? There is none today in Harlem. There's some places that you can dance, and they have half-ass entertainment. Some have food and entertainment, but you can't dance. There's not one with the combination of everything.

"I'd like to get a very large brownstone, have it gutted, you know, and on the first floor can be a restaurant. Second floor can be where the bar area is. Top floor can be entertainment. So you can spend an entire evening right there.

There's no real good restaurant anymore in Harlem. No place where you can really get dressed and take your woman to eat. And it would make a fortune, because, well, black people really like to get dressed up, man. They work hard all week, and they like to get dressed up, get superfly. And they have no place to go except some little cheesy, ratty bar."

People open restaurants all the time, of course, and I had no good reason to doubt that Jimmy could. But always in his presentation of parts of the dream there was a hint of quaintness. Sometimes it glinted in the words and phrases, sometimes in his clothes—more hipster than mod—sometimes in his woman, straight from the Middle West, from a life more careful.

"Jimmy," I said, "aren't the streets getting meaner all the time, isn't that one reason why people don't go out? Even *you* told me not to leave my car out there at night."

"People talk about that, but I don't think that's so, being out there in it all the time. People want to go out, but there's no place to go."

He agreed that the opening of restaurants and hotels downtown to black people had hastened the demise of the good old spots in Harlem.

"But that's why I imagine it would take a hundred thousand dollars to make it superfly," he said, "cause it's got to be fabulous. Like, ooooh, you know. Cause I'm charging top dollar, and you will get what you pay for.

"I don't let the rackets get in. Hey, can you imagine somebody trying to come into my joint with a racket? I would be independent. Why can't you be independent?"

"The mob runs the tablecloth service," I said.

"I don't need the mob. Why not have your own laundry? You have a basement, you have a cleanup crew, why not your own laundry? Guys hire a service because it's easier, but I want to do my own because I want it to be *just so*.

177

Have you ever been into a big restaurant where they have everything washed and ironed and they still have big stains and look nasty? I wouldn't want that."

"I understand that the mob can make it difficult to get licenses," I said.

"Oh, they probably know who to pay off to get your licenses faster, but I wouldn't even go down that trail. Like they might know who to see, they might say go see so-and-so, tell them we sent you, give him X amount of dollars, and you get your license right away without going through any changes. But if a guy comes in off the street and he's clean and nobody sent him, he's got to get a license too, eventually. It may take a lot longer, but so what?

"So then I get my license. After you get your license, fuck them all. What's the mob gonna do? Gonna have no numbers in my place. If I caught a bitch turnin a trick out of my place I'd break her leg. Be super-honest. My place would be so legal they couldn't touch it. Cause if you start paying off, you're gonna end up paying off. So I'm not gonna start. And I've got enough street background so that if you come in my place and fuck around, I'm not so nice or so lily white that I wouldn't think of having your fucking ribs kicked in."

Jimmy stood up and paced, in seeming reverie.

"You got to be of a certain caliber to come into my club. I'm not taking any riff-raff off the street. It's not a bar anybody can just walk into and ask for a drink. It's a club. Your attire must be just so. No, man, you cannot come in without a tie on. No, you cannot come in with a sweater-shirt, I don't care how slick you think you look. There are certain requirements. Now, if you come in without a tie on, you got to have a turtleneck and jacket. . . ."

I pointed out to him that a sweater-shirt was his own style, but he waved it off, and I agreed it was not relevant.

"Do you really know any hustlers making it this way?" I asked.

"Sure. It's all around you. You remember my ex-supplier that retired. And I know, by name at least, a young fellow about twenty-five years old, he's doin it. Dig what he bought this year: four Eldorados for his four top lieutenants, two Mark III's for his two top men, and a Rolls-Royce for himself. Now, when you can buy cars like that, you're making it.

"Now, my partner," he continued in a voice more subdued, "okay, he's doing bad right now, but that's a question of scag. Smart dealers in scag don't use it, cause it fucks up your business. He's making money, but he's losing it. I guess of the people I hang out with, I'm the most successful guy I know. I would hope to be able to get it together within the next six months. By then I should have enough money to try to do a little something, not by myself maybe, but with a couple partners."

"A hundred thousand dollars?"

"Well, if things go good for six months, I can have enough to get down with a couple people and do something. Not a hundred thousand worth maybe, but something nice. I got a couple of things in the workings, with people who have big money. When I say big money, I mean big enough to give me twenty or thirty thousand dollars' backing for X amount of time. And I would invest it in my hustle thing, make that twenty into forty, then forty into eighty. And it would be advantageous to somebody with some cash laying around to invest it in my thing. And while I'm turning these investments over, I can be getting together a legal hookup, a club or something. Cause if people will invest money with me on something that's illegal, where anytime I can take a fall and their money is down the drain—if they'll do that, then you *know* they'll invest in something like a club."

"Christmas is coming on," I said.

"Yeah?"

"That's when you first told me you were aiming to be out by."

"Yeah, well, even *before* I met you I had set a goal of September. Then I extended it to Christmas. Now I expect to retire by next spring. Hey, listen: I *know* hustling is not a career. You do it, get your money, and be cool, cause otherwise you're going to jail or get shot. But it doesn't take very long if you just get out there and do it."

"Hey you guys," Phyl called from the kitchen, "the food's ready."

Jimmy slapped his knee and got up. "Well, if I can't get my money from backers, then I won't. I'll have to do it my way, slowly. And then you know what? I think I might move into a nice fly building up in Riverdale, in the Bronx. I'm not ready to own a house yet. Cause they're a lot of trouble, man. Grass to cut and stuff. I guess I could have people doing it for me, but I'm not that wealthy yet. I'm a do-it-yourselfer anyway. I like to do things, but I don't have the time. Further out in the country where it's quiet—yeah, I could dig that sometimes, but only for the weekend. But Riverdale is close enough, and I don't want to be too far away from the city. I'd like to rent a home, maybe something with the option to buy. But it would have to be a fly house, would have to be pretty, else I wouldn't have it. Riverdale is residential, it's pretty, it's a nice place to raise a kid. I'm not gonna raise a kid in a tenement."

"You-all comin to the table?"

"Yeah, baby, right now."

16

Jimmy held in front of him, for me to see, a clear plastic bag of shiny crystalline pure cocaine that weighed 425 grams, a little less than a pound. The bag, he said, had cost him $4,400.

Jimmy was now buying pure coke.

"I told you," he said, smiling with satisfaction, "that things were going to be better and better. I didn't used to buy pure cocaine, and now I do." He raised his eyebrows, and I nodded.

He put a china dinner plate on his lap, dipped into the bag with a measuring spoon, and put a quarter of pure coke on the plate. From opaque plastic quart bottles on the table he took a tablespoon of lactose and one of dextrose and added them to the plate. He borrowed a plastic pocket calendar from me and with it began mixing the three elements together, his hand moving back and forth over the white mound in short, quick chopping motions. He scraped the mound together and chopped across it again and again, putting the coke on a two for his personal use. On the street, the mound of cut coke would be worth at least $450. Ordinarily he would not have this coke in his home. But people were nervous about me going to the stash, and so for my benefit he was presenting this show of progress in his living room.

"I used to sell ten-dollar blows," he said, teasing the cocaine with the plastic card, and me with his smile. "But no more."

He wasn't wearing his gold spoon, so he creased a matchbook cover and scooped up a bit of the mix. He snorted a two-and-two and nodded. "Now, coke like that, with a two on it, soldiered right through. That is good coke."

"So now you're buying pure," I said.

"Mmm-hmm."

"What happened?"

He chuckled. "I got bankrolled."

"You really have a backer?"

"Mmm-hmm."

"Why is he backing you?"

"He believes. He believes. He's done what I'm trying to do. He's successful. So I guess he feels he can make it on my success too. It's a good investment. If you invest, let's say, ten thousand dollars for sixty days, and you can make twenty thousand—where can you do that in the street? Now, when I say sixty days, you know who's getting the benefit of *that*. Cause in sixty days I should be able to *triple* the money. I'm gonna try to make it four times as much. Shit, I gotta make some money too, since I'm doin all the work. And if I do it very carefully and good, it can happen. I've never had a backer before. Let me show you something."

Jimmy took from the end table a little black notebook in which he had his balance sheet. He held it between us and traced down the list of first names and dollar figures with his index finger. He paused at one name, which I recognized, beside which was written "$1,500." He slowly drew his finger back and forth under that name and figure.

"That's a lot for a guy to be into you for," I said.

His satisfaction remained undiminished. "Cordin to what you're spending. If a guy's spending two thousand dollars, then fifteen hundred is too much. But if he's spending four or five thousand, then fifteen hundred is just the profit money."

He reached over to the end table and from under a towel

took a .38 Smith & Wesson snub-nosed revolver, and six bullets. "See this? I think maybe you've seen this gun before. But look at the bullets."

They were hollow-tipped, the kind that blow open inside and leave a bigger hole where they exit than they did where they entered.

"This is a kill gun," he said soberly. "See, copping what I'm copping now could put me in prison for life, if I was caught. Hey, I'm not going to prison. So there are certain situations that would call for a shoot-out. So when I'm copping these amounts, I carry this gun. And I would kill anybody that tried to stop me."

Jimmy hissed and shook his head. "You know, this administration is insane. They actually believe that if they make the penalties stiffer, they're going to get the dealers. Hey, listen: Have you been digging how many cops have been shot in the last couple weeks? Nine cops! Now, doesn't that say something to you? You come upon me to bust me now, and that bust means I will serve a minimum of twenty-five years in prison, all the way to *life!* I would be almost sixty years old when I came out, at the earliest. So what does that say? That says that when you bust somebody like that, he's going to try to kill you. Let me tell you something. I think I would rather die in a shootout than go to prison for twenty-five years. That's what this administration doesn't understand. Do you really believe that I would go to prison for that length of time? Here I would be, a sixty-year-old nigger with no education. No, no, no. I would rather kill a cop."

He tucked the gun into a black holster that had no belt, just a metal clip, like on a steel tape measure, on the back. "You know how you wear this?" he asked.

"Nope."

"Just loosen your belt a bit." I complied. "Now, tuck this on the inside of your pants with the clip over your belt." I

183

complied again. "Now, put your jacket on, and it's gone." It was true.

Jimmy took the gun back and put it down beside him. He picked up the phone and dialed a number. The person he wanted was not there, and he listened to some explanation, then put the phone down.

"Well, can you imagine that," he said, tilting his head back and looking straight up, then looking at me. "Did you know that today was Black Solidarity Day?"

Buying pure cocaine raised the specter of organized crime. Jimmy's view of his suppliers always was, "I treat 'em as individuals." In this case, now, on Black Solidarity Day, I pushed it.

"How about individuals getting rich on Harlem's blood," I said, "even the blood of the kids?"

"Hey, listen!" He faced me directly and gestured with a half-closed fist and an index finger. "You talk about getting rich on Harlem's blood. In Harlem the average income is about four thousand dollars or some shit like that. So you go in Harlem and buy a fryer, you know, a chicken, you spend a dollar and some change—say one-sixty for the sake of argument. Go over to the suburbs where the income is say fifteen thousand a year and buy a fryer of better quality for ninety cents. Now, that says it. Kids in Harlem get used to inferior shit—food, clothes, shoes, everything—it's all cheaper in the richer neighborhoods. If you were a kid in Harlem, what would that say to you? Somebody's exploiting the shit out of you! You think the kids here don't know that? It's not me that's exploiting Harlem."

"But you *are* dealing with racists."

"Oh there's cats I know who are uptight because I am black. I can see it in their faces. I get very sensitive and uptight about it, but I don't let it show. But then it works both ways. I know cats that I do business with that are black that are just as racially motivated—hey! as bigoted as white fellows that didn't dig me. I guess you're liberal-minded or whatever and you figure the black cause is justified. Shit yeah, I do too. I *know* it's justified. But the only point is that, hey man, I'm equal because I'm a man as much as you are. Now, if I had as much education as you had, we'd be on the same level. I don't give a fuck what color you are. But for me to say that I'm better than you because I'm black, I don't agree with that either. A man is a man. You can't be better than a man just because you're black, although it might be advantageous to be black nowadays, you know."

On the subject of black and white, it seemed to me there was often missing a certain *spark* to his rhetoric, that flash of passion one sees in many eyes these days. It was as if his business, despicable in many Harlem eyes, had caused a subtle detachment.

"The Black Panthers are pretty tough on people who deal drugs," I said. "How can you talk to a Panther about your racial consciousness?"

"You're talking about *dope* again," he said with some agitation, his eyes now showing a spark. "I don't fuck with scag! That's not part of my operation. It's not my shot. My partner, sure. But I don't touch that personally. How many times a year do you hear about people O.D.-ing on coke? It just doesn't happen." His voice softened slightly. "That's how I wash my conscience on *that*."

He leaned forward, eyes narrowed. "Listen. Some dude comes up to me and tells me about what I'm doin and gives me some shit, he's fuckin around and he's gonna get hurt. If I stopped doing what I'm doing, will it stop the money from going out of Harlem? If I stopped doing it, somebody else would go in and start. I have never seen a pusher go up to a junkie and say buy my dope, or I'm gonna bust you in the head. I have known a lot of pushers, and I have never known a pusher say to *anybody,* kids or whatever, come on and try my dope.

"Dig this: I know a motherfucker that sells dope to kids. He's about twenty-two, and his whole clientele is about fourteen to twenty-one. He's told motherfuckers, 'Hey listen, you're clean, don't start shootin.' But kids come, you know, and say they wanna try some dope. He might say, 'Look, if you wanna fuck with it, snort it, don't start shootin it.' Then some do and some don't. Now, if you want to buy, he'll sell it to you."

"You talk about it almost as if it were a public service," I said.

"Public service? Sure it is. It's entertainment." A smile came and went. "Hey, you know what would happen if all the dope dealers suddenly stopped selling dope? In Harlem? Do you realize that sixty percent of the black population, I would say, is hooked on drugs? They would get uptight and wouldn't have no dope. It would be a bitch in this town, for a long enough period to destroy the town. Oooh, man. You ever see a junkie couldn't get no dope? That's when he becomes dangerous. Junkie's a passive cat. Junkie shoots up and you could take him by the hand and lead him down the garden path and he'd go for it. But let him have no dope and he becomes sick physically, and a dangerous motherfucker."

"Would you consider taking your coke operation downtown?"

"Downtown where? Midtown Manhattan? And go to jail? When you don't be in Harlem to sell coke, you sell coke to white people. I don't know them like I know black people. I wouldn't try. Not unless I knew them personally."

"What if you had white guys working for you to take it downtown?"

"Again that's dangerous. I wouldn't be able to go downtown and check on 'em at will. I wouldn't know their clientele. I wouldn't know whether they'd turn me into the police. It would be dangerous, man. I have white cats that I do business with, but I *know* them. But they wouldn't come into Harlem and try to sell dope. Would you come into Harlem and try to sell dope if you were a dealer? Just like you'd be conspicuous here, I'd be conspicuous downtown, I imagine. There'd be a lot of resentment for various reasons, you know. It would cause a lot of static, I think. I don't need it."

"You will not deny," I said, "that the harm is being done, that kids are using dope, and that the money goes out of Harlem and gets back to the Mafia."

"*I* am not selling dope to kids. *I* am not selling dope to junkies. I am not selling a habit. Sure, some people might say what you're saying. But a lot of those same people, they're hungry. How can you be a do-gooder or a righteous-righteous if you're hungry? How can you tell me I shouldn't sell coke when you don't know where the fuck the next month's rent is coming from? Ha!"

It was hard to imagine Jimmy dealing with white people wearing white ties and silk suits, although since drug dealers trade with organized crime at some point up the line, and Jimmy is a drug dealer, one can reasonably deduce it to be so. I would say from time to time on various points, "Are you telling me the truth?" And then I would immediately realize the naïveté of the question. There was always an element of implicit peril—professional, philosophical, physical—in either believing him or not believing him. Better, then, to push forth and look back later for patterns by which to judge.

"Do you know how and where your product comes into the country?" I asked.

"I'm not supposed to, nor do I need to, but I do. I try to make it my business to know. The more you know, the more you are in a position to dicker. Like when you know a shipment's coming in, you know that if you go just when it's com-

187

ing in you're gonna get a better deal, cause they're fat. And if you go toward the end of it, when not much is left, then you'll probably get a little less quality. It works that way even when you're buying keys. I'm greedy. I want the best for my buck so I can make the most."

"How and where does it come in?"

"Can't tell you that. My man just gets coke. He doesn't bring it in. It's brought to him by somebody who's working for someone on his level out of the country. I think my man is the top man in his organization in coke. That is to say, anybody in his organization that wants coke has to go to him, no matter what level they're on. But as far as being able to have the last word about policy, there are a couple people above him that have the last word as far as policy goes."

"Tell me about your man. What's he like?"

"Well, he's my main supplier. I had two good ones. I have six or seven that I can go to, but I only had these two that were reliable. Now I have one, because the other one retired. Right now my man's got about sixteen keys. In a way, I think he's kind of a big freak. I think he gets his thing off dealing with the underworld. He doesn't have to financially. He's a very wealthy man. I believe he's got over a million. But he doesn't get hooked up, he's not flashy, no diamonds. He wears dungarees and shit like that. I don't know how he built his thing up, but he's got a couple legitimate businesses. Cat is very down to earth, very nice people, he snorts, smokes. We're friends. Like I go to his house for dinner. I know his wife and kids. I can go up anytime and like, 'Hey man, I'm tired,' and he'll say to just lay down on the couch and sleep. I wouldn't necessarily have to have rapport with the cat to deal with him, but I do."

"When you make a connection, you call him and meet him here or there?"

"Never here, never there. Wouldn't do any shit like that

in my house. That's dangerous. We use the car, restaurants, parks, highways."

"Suppose you got into trouble," I said, "could you go to your man with your problems?"

Jimmy nodded. "Uh, cordin to what the problem was. I would tell it to him and he would evaluate it. I know if I got into a jam they'd bail me out, you know, without a doubt. Like they'd go so far as to rough somebody off for me. I would not necessarily need to tell them why. I had some problems with a cat once, you know, Slick and I, and that's when I was told, 'When do you want him hit?' "

"You could ask for somebody to be hit?"

He shrugged modestly. "I didn't know I could. But he said, 'It's up to you. Use your own discretion from now on.' If there was a hit needed, he would make all the arrangements for it, and he went on to tell me, you know, I can call for it."

"Then why do you get involved with buying a silencer and so forth?"

"Cause I don't go to him all the time with my problems. That's why they dig me, that's why things are cool. I take care of me. Who wants my headaches? I take care of my own shit. Except, well, there are certain kinds of problems. . ."

"What kinds of problems?"

Jimmy sighed and rubbed his hands over his eyes. "Special kinds."

"Such as?"

"Mmm. Well, like if I found out that Richard is a cop, an undercover narco bull. That would be a very special problem. I might need some help on that. Whole lot of shit that could get me in very big fucking trouble. Cause see, then it's not just *me*. Whole lot of shit could come down if you had been running everything back to the cops. I would have to tell the people above me that this dude I know is an

189

undercover cop. And then I would have to explain what I had been doing. And that might get me killed. Unless, well, I'd probably have to tell them that I had just killed *you*, which might mean that they wouldn't kill me. They might not. Maybe they would just send me somewhere for a couple of years or something. But they'd be very upset."

17

"You better get in touch with Jimmy," a friend advised me. "Things are really jumping off for him, better than he ever imagined they would. He's got a chauffeur now, and he's talking about opening some club or shit. He's really flying."

"I've been trying to reach him," I said, "but he doesn't call back when he says he will, and I usually get no answer when I call him."

"Yeah," the friend said. "I don't know about his head. He's forgetting things, and he's even sleeping through the telephone, which he never used to do. Cat *never* sleeps, all that runnin, all that coke. But things are moving for him. I mean *really*."

We had an appointment at ten o'clock one morning, and I arrived and went through the lobby door, which was unlocked, and rode the elevator up to his floor and pushed his doorbell. Jocko barked from his bathroom pen, but I could hear nothing else stirring. I decided to wait.

Twenty minutes later the elevator door opened and Jimmy strode out jauntily, his applejack cap tilted forward, his hands in the pockets of a new knee-length coat which had a fur collar. He smiled.

"That's good timing, huh?" he said, unlocking the door. "Been out all night. I just came back to see you and change my clothes and go right back out again."

"You're really running," I said, trotting along behind him to the bedroom.

"Yeah. There is a real panic out there. Been no coke any-place, not *anywhere* for three days. Was a real famine. People been hollerin for coke. Now I can get it again, and everybody wants it. Got to strike. Really movin it now." He hung up his coat.

"I understand you have a chauffeur."

"Yeah, cat owed me some money, so I took him *and* his car."

As if that reminded him, he went to the phone and called the chauffeur, directing him to "be around" at a certain evening hour.

"Yeah, I'm buying a car for Phyl—you know, she's going to get her driver's license. I think I'll get her a sports car. And for me . . ." He smiled. "Maybe a big Jag. That would be my Sunday-go-to-meetin car."

He chuckled and went over to the dresser. From the top drawer he took what looked like a thick silver pen. He held it out toward me, then snapped it open to expose a small cartridge chamber.

"I had it made for me," he said. "It can take a twenty-two bullet, but I keep it loaded with Mace." He put a handful of tiny purple pellets on the dresser top. "Those are Mace," he said. "They are actually more effective than twenty-two bullets, because a twenty-two bullet may not stop you."

He set himself up in the center of the room, legs apart. "A dude comes on you to take you off or whatnot. Now, if this was loaded with a twenty-two bullet I might be able to snap it out of my pocket and fire it, but it might not even slow you down. But with Mace . . ." He made a quick move to the side, ducked—"Tcheew"—he clicked the pen—"and then bang!"—he drew and fired his index finger from a crouched position. "See, Mace will stop you right away, for long enough for me to draw and hit you with something better, like this thirty-two." He held now in his hand a thirty-two automatic that had also been in the dresser drawer.

"Actually," he said, "this thirty-two is not for me. This is for Phyl, you know, to keep here in the drawer. I think a girl needs protection around here. Shit, you never know when some junkie or rapist or something will start fiddling with the lock."

"Phyl is going to use a *gun?*" I asked, incredulous, imagining her black hair flowing over her shoulders, her soft brown hands wrapped around the thirty-two, her eyes closed as she pulled the trigger.

"Sure. I'll teach her how. If somebody got in here or something, she could call the police, but by the time they got here, whew! I think she ought to have some protection."

He picked up the "pen" again and opened it to show me the working parts. He put a twenty-two caliber bullet in the chamber to show the fit. "Ain't this something?" he said, smiling. "I'll get you one if you want."

He went to the closet and started pushing aside clothes, then abruptly spun around and snapped his fingers and rushed to the other side of the room and pulled open a dresser drawer. "Let me show you. Let me *show* you!" He pulled out an assortment of paraphernalia relating to a new hobby he had discovered, a hobby which seemed perfectly to blend his interests in art and technology. I laughed at his brazenness at even attempting this new form of expression. He smiled proudly and turned his attention back to clothes while I went through the new display. The telephone chimed intermittently. On most calls he simply mumbled a few phrases and hung up. One call was from Slick, and Jimmy invited him to come by. He also invited another caller to drop by. He gave yet another caller a status report, including the comment that he was planning to open a nightclub in a large midwestern city.

"Whew!" I said. "I heard things were going well."

"Yeah. I think I will move up to Riverdale in the spring." He brought out some possible evening selections and laid the clothes over the bed.

193

"I've been calling you a lot in recent days," I said.

"Really? What time?"

"Lots of different times. Nine in the morning, ten, eleven, eight in the evening. I get no answer."

"Yeah, you know why? I been having trouble with the phone. Sometimes it rings for the caller, but doesn't ring here."

"I thought maybe you had been sleeping through it."

"Nope. I hear it if it rings."

"What about that day you were going to call me back?"

"Oh yeah. I tried to reach you. There was no electricity in the apartment. It was freezing cold. I had to get out. So we couldn't meet."

The doorbell rang, and Jimmy opened it to let in a young man dressed in a loose-necked sweater, slacks, and desert boots. He joined us in the bedroom as Jimmy continued his clothing ritual. He introduced the man as a law student and said, "He's going to be my lawyer, no shit." He continued to lay out combination after combination as he chattered about photography, friends, business. Greens, browns, and yellows were matched and switched in a parade of shirts, trousers, shoes, hats, coats.

"Hey," Jimmy said, suddenly interrupting the fashion search. "You know what happened to me a couple days ago? Dig this: I got busted. Cops busted me for *armed robbery of a delicatessen!*"

"Armed *robbery?*"

Jimmy pulled from his closet a hanger over which there was a protective plastic bag. He removed that and held up a magnificent coat that looked like black sealskin. "Apparently what happened is that the cops were looking for a black dude with a cap and a black coat. And they stopped me cause I was wearing *this*. Dig it: I was wearing this coat, driving an Eldorado, had eleven hundred dollars in my pocket, and they were hassling me for sticking up a grocery store and taking seventy dollars, just cause I had on the right hat and coat."

"What happened with it?"

Jimmy hissed. "Judge threw it right out because it wasn't real."

He put the coat back and laid across the bed an ensemble consisting of green trousers and a yellow shirt. On the floor beneath the dangling pants legs he placed a pair of black alligator shoes.

"What you think?"

I said nothing. The law student was not so reluctant. "I think that's a little bright, Jimmy, I mean, you know, yellow and green."

"But you got to understand this," Jimmy said without hesitation. "The image is important. It's the image." He put up his hand like a traffic cop giving a stop signal. "Hey, I'm not dealing with lawyers, you know."

The law student laughed.

"It's true," Jimmy said to me. "Certain things in the image are important, certain things about style are important to know on the street. There are little things. Like, do you know why black men wear mustaches? Because in slavery days they weren't allowed to. So it became a way of showing their masculinity. Lot of black men who wear mustaches don't even know that."

He looked down at the clothes on the bed and rubbed his chin. Then he looked up abruptly. "Hey, you know what? I'm going to do some modeling, you know, clothes. I dig that. I'm building my wardrobe to it. Shit yeah, I know there's a lot of fags in it, but they don't bother me. I might start next week, or soon."

He looked once more at the yellow-and-green outfit on the bed, then snatched it up and hung it back in the closet.

Jimmy lit a reefer and leaned back, in what seemed to me

to be a rare mood of relaxation. He had had some sleep. He yawned and smiled. "Yeah, things were kind of rocky for a while. My money's gotten back together again. I got a couple new contacts, new connections, people that I cop from." He yawned again.

"White or black?" I asked.

"Neither," he said, laughing quietly, toying with me. "They're not white and they're not black."

"So what does that leave?"

"A whole host of shit." He yawned again. "They're *cubanos*."

"Is that good?"

"If *they're* good, that's good."

"So does that mean everything's going to get even better even faster now?"

He laughed again, an easy, soft laugh. "Not necessarily. Theoretically, but not necessarily. Cause of the amount of heat that's on out there. Got to be supercareful these days."

"You mean you can't deal the same way, in bars, or what?"

"Oh, you can go ahead and make all the deals you want. They only flag you in transportin the shit."

"Well, you *have* to transport it."

"It has to *be* transported. Somebody has to transport it *for* you."

"If it's so hot," I said, "why would anybody else want to take that risk?"

"Cause if *you* get busted carrying shit for me, I can get you out on bail. If *I* get busted, everything is all over for everybody."

Neither of us said anything for a few moments as he smoked down to the roach. Then he laughed again, a friendly, real chuckle. "Sounds reasonable," he said then, raising his eyebrows and looking at me. "Sounds good anyway, right? Hey, things are cool while they are cool."

196

18

It was a bitter-cold afternoon, and the air over the city was unusually clear. From the balcony high up in the apartment building you could see most of Central Park, the sun glinting off the frozen reservoir, and on east, the bridges over the East River in the distance telescoped by the eye so that they seemed to be resting upon each other. Farther yet, airplanes, no more than silver slivers, were low in the air over La Guardia Airport. To the right, the spires and glass of midtown, silver and gold in the low light.

It is such a view, I thought, that makes it possible for one to believe he could own a city.

Jimmy stood in the cold and spread his arms as if to gather up the entire vision. "Oooh, hey," he said. "Phyl has got to see this."

He and I went back in, and he took Phyl out to the balcony. They stood together, silhouetted in the shadow of the balcony above. Seen from inside the large window, they were a silent vision, a pantomime against the skyline, he slowly tracing the horizon with his hand, she nodding slightly, hunched against the cold. Then they came back in.

"Wow!" he said. "I want me a view like that. That is unbelievable."

There was a possibility of a vacancy in the building, and Jimmy went off with the host to discuss it.

His arrival at the apartment had been truly an *arrival*. Into the room of modly dressed friends he strode, ushering

Phyl before him, and then he stood, for a masterful moment, still.

"Hey Jim," said one of the handful of friends seated around, "you look like you been invited to the *fights* or something."

The allusion to the recent boxing bouts of Muhammad Ali, where a style of male elegance in dazzling furs and plumage had been the hit of the arenas, didn't disturb Jimmy's entrance. He was wearing his knee-length black leather coat over a black pony-hide shirt, tight black trousers, black shoes, and black gloves. He took off his coat. His coke spoon hung around his neck outside his shirt, the gold of it contrasting so starkly with the black as to give it an almost reverent air, like a cross.

"Hey Jim, no shit, you goin to the fights?"

The snickering was not unfriendly teasing, and Jimmy accepted it or ignored it as he moved to room center. For a time he dominated the room with commentary about progress in his hobby, and on how a persistent swelling in his scarred ankle would preclude his joining the others on the ski slopes the following morning.

And then the status report, which was delivered to me, but not confidentially. "Let's see, what's today, the fifteenth? Okay. Since the first of the month I've lost nine G's, nine G's."

I sat beside Phyl on the sofa, and he stood before us. "Hey, you know what that broad did?" he said, tapping my knee with his knuckles. "You know what Phyl did? We were angry at each other, just before we went away for the holidays. She was really angry." He bent forward and lowered his voice as if to share a joke. "She got out of a cab and left two thousand dollars' worth of jewelry in there, two thousand dollars' worth of jewelry in the cab. Can you dig that? Cause she was angry and wasn't thinking."

He smiled smugly, and I looked at Phyl, and she nodded

in confirmation while looking more or less at the floor. "It was just in a bag," she said, "with no identification or anything. It was really some nice things, fourteen-carat gold earrings and some nice rings and stuff. Stuff somebody else could easily use, you know, could give to his wife. So Jimmy told me not even to bother going to the precinct about it. It was really some pretty jewelry, just in a bag on the seat."

"Yeah," Jimmy said, now back in the center of the room. "And you know that big gold bracelet I used to wear, with the diamonds that spelled my name? I lost it last week. That's another grand. And then, you know, some stuff in the business."

"So things have really been bad, huh?" I said. "Nine grand in two weeks."

It was the question he wanted, and he smiled in satisfaction. We drifted away from the sofa, and now his tone became confidential.

"What I'm telling you is that I lost nine grand in two weeks, and I still bought six thousand dollars' worth of equipment [for his hobby], and I bought a leather coat, and I'm buying Phyl a car, and last night I bought a key of coke and four pounds of reefer. Sometimes now I'm buying four or five keys of coke. That's what I'm telling you. That's all *including* dropping nine G's."

Now Jimmy had gone to check on the apartment. The other men sat near the broad window, snorting coke from time to time from an open pouch of aluminum foil on the coffee table, rolling joints from the pile of marijuana on a paper plate, drinking Löwenbräu beer, and talking about the Super Bowl, which was coming up and in which some of their friends would be playing.

I sat with Phyl on the sofa, sharing reminiscences of the Midwest, where we both were born. The gentle discomfort earlier between us, caused by the fact that I was not really a friend yet had the queer license to probe and be around, had dissipated over the weeks, and we talked more naturally. And together we actually shared a more similar world than either of us did with the others in the room.

"He didn't really yell, you know," she said. "I was more sorry to lose the jewelry than he was." Her words were always gently presented, like her clothes and her manners and her smiles. She had that casual innocence of those few in Jimmy's world who, with strange detachment, well perceived the man but not the business. "You know how he is. He tries to *sound* so bad."

She looked around. "This is very nice," she said of the apartment. "I *really* don't like it where we live. You know, it's so dark. I can't even grow plants. And then that neighborhood, you know. I don't like going into the apartment alone. I'd like to move. I'd kind of like a house, you know, but Jimmy doesn't feel ready for it. He needs to be closer, you know, around here, just now. A house would be too far away, he says."

Jimmy and the host returned, and it seemed that, with a string pulled and a few dollars passed, Jimmy could have a similar apartment.

"We'll be moving in four weeks," Jimmy said.

He was excited, and made another tour of the apartment with the host, gesturing, sizing up, imagining rugs, draperies, colors, his hands placing a sofa here, a room divider there "so somebody coming in the door can't see your whole crib right away," rearranging the stereo speakers. Only the view was left out of his voluble designing, for it was the view around which all was being designed. That and Phyl. He took her by the hand and made yet another tour.

Then he came back, and went to look out the window again. "I'm going to build me a ranch house when I get ready," he said, "up in Riverdale or somewhere. Down *there* maybe." He pointed down to an apparently free plot of grass across the street from Central Park, among the tall buildings. "I'm going to get really really high and design a fantastic ranch for myself. There's plenty of room around."

Jimmy went to get his coat, put it on, and came back to the window. As we were standing there, the host came up and glowered at Jimmy. "I hope you got a two on you," the man said gruffly, "cause this stuff you sold me yesterday ain't worth shit."

Jimmy stood looking stonily at the man, his hands in his pockets.

"I mean it. It ain't worth shit. I ain't even gonna use it."

Jimmy spoke in carefully enunciated tones. "Well, that's what I got. That's what I was going to pull out of my pocket. So if you feel that way, I won't pull it out."

The man snorted and turned away. Jimmy watched him. His hands remained in his pockets, and business was apparently concluded.

Pizzas, for which Phyl had expressed a hunger, arrived in the arms of a friend, and everybody scooped up a slice except Jimmy, who waved off the bid with an impatient flutter of his hand. He had been up for a couple of days, was thinking about the apartment, about things he had to do, and he wanted to get on with it.

"Come on, Phyl," he said with a trace of annoyance, which deepened when he saw her chomping on a pizza slice. "Why do you have to eat that stuff *now?*" he muttered through gritted teeth. Phyl finished and donned her coat. As she exchanged good-byes, Jimmy rolled his eyes upward in impatience. "Come on," he said sharply at last, and they waved and left.

In seconds he was back, to get his black gloves. "If I get a place like this," he whispered, heading again for the door, "she'll *never* leave me." He chuckled and went out.

"We're not going to take it," Phyl told me over the phone. "It's just too much money. It would cost about $550, plus we would need garage space for at least one, and probably two, cars. That's just too much right now. Don't you think that's a lot?"

"I guess it depends on how much you can afford," I said. "It doesn't seem like too high a price for that place."

"Well, I just think it's risky to start spending that much until things, you know, settle down, until Jimmy gets, well, until things are a little more stable."

"Have you definitely decided not to take the apartment?" I asked.

"Yeah, it's definite. We can find something cheaper. We'll just have to look around."

There was nothing ominous in the relaxed and pleasant atmosphere in the midtown living room. The peephole was opened and shut often as new drop-in guests were silently scrutinized, then let in. Dollar-bill pouches of coke were lying open on the table, in the kitchen, in the bathrooms. Various guests took turns rolling joints from the raw weed on a plate. Soft soul music came from the hi-fi, and the living room was dark except for the dim light which overflowed from the kitchen and hallway.

Then Jimmy arrived, dressed in a sheepskin coat and carrying a leather bag. But he didn't stop to say hello to anyone. There was anger and steel in his face, and he moved quickly down the hallway into a back bedroom, followed by two associates (business was now being done on a scale approaching ten kilos a month).

Those in the living room continued as before. An hour or so later Jimmy appeared at the corner of the room and motioned for me to join them in the back.

The partners reflected in their taut faces and fidgeting hands and deep breathing and sighs a crisis just past. On the tabletop, next to the balance scale and containers of pure coke and cut was Jimmy's bag, open. In it were his .357 Magnum, a pair of smaller pistols, the .32 Baretta automatic, and a foot-long black silencer. When Jimmy lifted his arms to rub his eyes, he revealed the butt of his nine-millimeter automatic stuck into his trouser holster. A few remaining beads of sweat glistened beneath his knit under-shirt.

"Whew!" he said, stretching. "That was close. Sorry I didn't recognize you when I came in, but I was so coked up. It was really close, man." One of his partners nodded as he opened a little plastic pill bottle and tapped some coke onto the back of his hand and snorted it. Then he went out. The other man sat on the edge of the bed, head drooped, a reefer in his hand. Then he looked up at Jimmy. "Yeah, man," he said.

"It had come to a kill thing, Richard," he said, sniffing between the words. "You almost had yourself something. See, this dude sold me some bogus shit, and I actually came here to set it up. I was going to leave here and kill him, me and a couple workers. But we made some phone calls and found out that it wasn't this dude's fault. I'll get my money back. But, oh man, that was close." He sniffed again. "That's why I was so coked up."

There was a knock on the bedroom door, and Jimmy opened it to let in a friend. Then he quickly dipped into his plastic bottle with his spoon and shoved the spoon under the friend's nose. The friend snorted, then winced. Tears came to his eyes, and he grinned at Jimmy, mopping a tear under one eye with his hand. "You love to do that to people, don't you," he said, sniffing to clear his nose of the pure cocaine he had just snorted.

Jimmy chuckled. "Shit, that's why you came in here, right? You guys come in here to get it, then you complain if I give it to you. Or if I *don't,* then you go out in the hall and start jivin about how I won't give you no blow."

Jimmy's ledger books were spread open on the table in front of him, but his hands were motionless beside them.

Jimmy nodded, on the edge of sleep; his eyelids floated up and down. Then his head snapped up, and he rubbed his eyes.

"Whew!" he said. "Man oh man oh man." He puffed out his cheeks and blew out a long breath.

"How long have you been up?" I asked.

"Couple days," he said, staring down at the ledger.

"I'm just curious," I said, "but why don't you snort some coke?"

He smiled demurely. "I'm trying *not* to," he said. "I like to train my body to do things without coke. I don't like for my body to *force* me to do anything."

He leaned back and rubbed his eyes and seemed to be reviving.

"You know what happened?" he said. "I went to the doctor. He said I was suffering from exhaustion, total exhaustion. Had to get some vitamin-B shots and shit. Guess I just got run-down. See, if I get four hours sleep a night, I'm fine. But I been goin two, three days with no sleep at all. Got to me, I guess."

He got up and stretched, then moved a little to Stevie Wonder singing "Signed, Sealed, and Delivered." "Aaah, yeah," he said. "Phyl wants me to go to work. Hey, since I'm not going to make a career of the street, I've *got* to. But when I do, aaah, I'm going to be very comfortable. Whatever I do is going to be a money-maker."

He sat down and stretched again. "Yeah, I'll get out of the street pretty soon. I'll be able to relax. Things will be cool."

He looked at me for a few seconds, then smiled. "Oh, okay." He took out his pill bottle of pure coke.

"You know what?" he said. "The street does certain things to me I don't like. I use a lot of profanity. I swear a lot, unnecessarily, which I don't like. I never did before. Being out there in the street makes a difference. Oh sure,

204

when I was a kid I used profanity because that's how you sounded like a grown-up. But there came a point in time when I realized that it wasn't necessary. You *got* to in the street. But it's very hard to turn it off when you come in your front door. I don't like to bring it home with me."

"Because of Phyl?"

"Not just that. I don't like it."

"Well, that's not the *worst* thing you do," I volunteered.

He shrugged.

"Tell me, Jim," I said. "Phyl never mentions directly what you do. But she must know, right?"

"Oh, she knows I fuck with it, hustling, but she doesn't like it. She's definitely against it. She wants me to go back to work, and she gets on me every now and then—hey, we're both Ariens, you know, born under the sign of Aries. But I find a way to squash it." He glanced at me with a wry smile. "I buy her dogs and diamonds. But then, she's in love. So I guess I can do things that she doesn't like but will accept, because she loves me. She knows I snort coke, and I guess she assumes that I must sell it or something. She doesn't talk about it, but she gets uptight. She knows I deal with reefer, but that's nothin. Everybody smokes reefer."

"Except Phyl."

"Heh-heh, yeah."

"Do you two talk about other girls?"

Jimmy lit up a reefer. He was thoughtful, his voice intimate.

"We've talked about other girls, and she says she knows I'm out on the street hustlin, and there may be a girl here and there, but she says just don't get anything going steady or serious."

He breathed deeply and tapped the ashes off into the ashtray. "Yeah, she puts up with a bit. I don't get as much time with her as she thinks I should—maybe once in a while I take her to the movies—and I really don't take as much time as *I know* I should." He took another deep drag. "But she's spoiled a bit too."

He got up and went over to the closet. "She'd kill me if she knew we were doing this," he said. He opened the door and dragged his arm through Phyl's wardrobe. He selected a few items and removed them from the rack and hung them on the door for me to see. Jumpsuits, pants suits, mini-dresses, silks, sweaters, furs, spangles, frills.

"Do you buy all these things for her?" I asked.

"Not everything. Sometimes our tastes are different. Like she doesn't like to get too flashy. She doesn't like a whole lot of diamonds and shit. But she dresses well, hmmm?"

We went back to the sofa and sat down and snorted some more coke.

"Do you ever think about your wife?"

He looked up, into the distance, showing with his eyes that he did for one reason or another. "Well, I loved her, my wife. I didn't really love her. But she hurt me, man, she hurt. She was a beautiful girl. I loved her beauty."

He looked at the living-room door. "J-o-c-k-o!" Jocko scampered back into the bathroom. "He's being punished. Peed on the floor again."

"I'll bet that you will be a strict father," I said.

"Well, I can't stand fresh children. So they can be obedient, but that's really because I just think you should get the most out of everything, really really. There'll be discipline. If I have a son, I'll whip his ass. You don't see black boys hittin their mothers or fathers. There's a certain respect. I had a real bad fight one time with a friend, an Italian boy, because he had hit his mother. But I think you can also be reasonable. If my son wants to get high, then I want to talk things over with him. I want him to get high with *me,* not someplace else. And not on scag, because I got a thing about scag, because of my childhood and all. But we always had a thing in our house: What happened in our house stayed in our house."

206

"Would you ever tell your son what you used to do?"

"Sure, if he was adult enough to be told in confidence. But I think you got to sit down and talk to your son about drugs and shit. I think you can talk about how the law was necessary to provide for the masses, but not every single individual. I mean, some laws are bullshit."

"What would happen to you if they legalized cocaine?"

He cocked his head and raised his palms in "C'est la vie" fashion. "It would stop my hustle. I'd go back to work, nine-to-five. No big thing. It would have been like a large vacation. I had a groovy time. Fuck it. Now, I might become a dangerous motherfuckin menace out on the street, because when you ain't got nothin to lose, you say fuck it, burn the building down, it ain't *my* building."

"But it wouldn't bother you to go back to work?"

"Not at all. I've worked all my life. Now, if I'd been a hustler all my life and never worked, it might scare me. But I've worked, man. If I became a millionaire, and then lost it all, you know what I'd be able to say to the motherfuckers? Hey man, I had it. You know how many people go through their life and can't say they had it? I hope I'm gonna keep it, of course, but to be able to say I had it—shit, that's more than most. That attitude keeps you from goin broke. I expect to work until I die. If I go back to work, you know how easy things become? I don't have to worry about the police. Oh man, my ulcer would go away. Hey man, I'd be straight! Course I wouldn't have nothin. I'd just be living from hand to mouth like every fuckin body else. Damn few make it big anyway. I know that."

Jimmy leaned back and opened his mouth to let some reefer smoke drift out. "You know what I want to do, really really? Go back to school. Get an education. I guess that sounds strange, huh? But that's important to me. I really want to."

More coke, more reefer, and he selected a record album and slid the record out. "But I look around me now, here, and I see I'm ten times richer than other cats I know who started like me in the slum, and I'm ten times richer than I was, or than I thought I'd be when I was workin nine-to-five."

The record was music behind some spoken words.

"And you'll get married someday," I said.

"Yup. Come with me."

I followed him into the bedroom. From Phyl's dressing table he took out a silver ring with two diamonds in it. "That's her engagement ring," he said. "She doesn't wear it because she's wearing another diamond, and she won't wear much jewelry." Then he held in front of me a second silver ring with a single diamond set in a fashion similar to the first ring. "This is the wedding ring," he said. "See, it's made to slip into the engagement ring, they fit together." He held up the double ring with three diamonds, then took them apart and put them away.

"Jimmy," I said as we returned to the living room, "have you ever killed anybody?"

I had asked him that before, and got wry smiles and arched eyebrows in reply. Others had told me he had. I felt now that he didn't want to say yes and he didn't want to say no, regardless of which was the truth. He sat down on the sofa and looked at me.

"I don't recommend it," he said softly. "It's not pleasant. It makes you sick, you know, all of a sudden there's a dude dead, who was alive, and then he's dead. Even though he might have deserved to die."

There were some moments of uncomfortable silence.

"Here we are," I said, "talking about love and marriage and children and all. And then about killing."

His face turned hard. "Look, I'm not a killer. My little brother has killed thirty or forty people in Vietnam. What's worse, killing somebody who's trying to kill you or who deserves to be killed, or throwing a grenade into a house and

208

killing a bunch of people who never did you *nothin?* That's just cold-blooded, man, that's what *killers* do."

There was another silence. "There've been a few," he said softly.

He got up to pace, then went over to the turntable to re-start the record he had put on earlier. "Hey, lie down on the floor," he said. He plugged in the earphones. "You really got to listen to this."

It was an album of love poems read by Arthur Prysock. As I lay there, Jimmy brought over the coke pouch and gave me that and a joint. Then he lit a thick beige candle and put it next to my nose.

"It's coconut," he said. "Phyl bought it for me because she knows I like coconut."

The aroma of the candle mixed with the love poems in a sensual swirl, and Jimmy smiled. When that record was fin-ished, he put on one of hard, bitter black poetry, poems of verbal knives so sharp it made me sit up. I rubbed the candle along my nose and listened closely. When it was finished we looked at each other with wide eyes.

"Whew," I said.

Jimmy crouched down in front of the row of record al-bums. "Hey, do you dig Bach?" he asked.

"Bach?"

"Yeah. You know, Johann Sebastian?"

"Sure."

He guided me to the velvet lounge chair and put the ear-phones on my head and then went back and put on a record of the Swingle Singers humming Bach. The music rose and fell and sprayed and splashed like a delicate sum-mer surf playing among the rocks. Jimmy hummed lightly with the melody, closed his eyes and danced and snapped his fingers and moved his shoulders to Bach. I held the candle.

Then he took the candle from me and poured the melted

209

wax from the top into a clean ashtray. When it stiffened, he peeled the piece out and gave it to me. "When you go," he said, "take this. Put it on top of the defroster in your car. In about two minutes your whole car will be ooooh!"

Six hours after I had arrived, I left, caressing the piece of candle in my pocket. I walked out onto the Harlem night street. My car was half a block away. Coming toward me were two large black men, one wearing a dashiki and one a fatigue jacket. They took the middle of the sidewalk, and I moved to the gutter to pass.

"Hey mister," I heard called behind me. I kept walking.

"Hey mister!" The voice was more insistent. I got to my car and went to the driver's side away from the sidewalk. As I put the key in the lock there was a thump on the roof. I snapped my head up.

"Hey."

It was B.J., in an Army jacket, leaning across my roof, extending his hand.

"B.J." I said. "You're back?"

"Yeah," he said. "I was in the hole down there for a while. Lost some weight. But now, back in business."

"I was just up to see your man," I said. There was a silence. "I hope everything goes okay," I said.

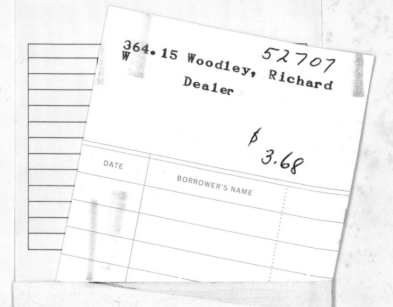

364.15 Woodley, Richard
W
    Dealer   52707

52707

364.15 Woodley, Richard
W
    Dealer

$3.68

DATE	BORROWER'S NAME	

© THE BAKER & TAYLOR CO.